LIFE IN THE ROMAN WORLD
ROMAN LEICESTER

Narrative and art: Giacomo Savani

Archaeological and historical context: Sarah Scott

Roman Leicester: Mathew Morris

The School of Archaeology and Ancient History (SAAH)

The School of Archaeology and Ancient History at the University of Leicester is home to a world-class, international team of scholars engaged in cutting-edge research and teaching. The School offers a wide range of campus-based undergraduate and postgraduate programmes and has a thriving Distance Learning community.

The sites, structures, art, landscapes and materials of the Roman world are core research strengths of the School of Archaeology and Ancient History. The archaeological and historical background in this book is based on our published research in these fields, and our distance learning teaching resources, which explore the diversity of Rome, its impacts and its legacies, both within the empire and beyond.

School of Archaeology and Ancient History, University Road, Leicester, LE1 7RH

www.le.ac.uk/archaeology

University of Leicester Archaeological Services (ULAS)

University of Leicester Archaeological Services (ULAS) is an award-winning professional archaeological unit based in the School of Archaeology and Ancient History at the University of Leicester. ULAS undertakes archaeological projects all over the UK, mostly connected with planning applications for new developments, road schemes and quarries. The unit has expertise in urban archaeology, and staff have been involved in almost all the major excavations that have taken place in Leicester over the past 35 years. This book is based on the excavations and publications of ULAS, whose work has transformed our understanding of Leicester from Roman to early modern times.

ULAS, School of Archaeology and Ancient History, University Road, Leicester LE1 7RH

www2.le.ac.uk/services/ulas/

Leicester Classics Hub

In partnership with Classics for All, our students and staff support state schools seeking to incorporate Classics within or alongside the curriculum. A key aim is to raise awareness that studying the archaeology, history and literature of the classical world can be embedded within many areas of the curriculum and can benefit pupils in many ways. This book is linked to our resources for KS2–5 which explore the cultural diversity of the Roman world. Our teaching resources incorporate hands-on activities based on a combination of SAAH research and local ULAS excavations and are available for download on our website.

classicsforall.org.uk

www.le.ac.uk/acc

Contents

Britain in the Roman world: archaeology

Archaeology is the study of the material remains of people who lived in the past. There is a wealth of archaeological evidence from the Roman era in Britain, including the remains of structures, evidence from aerial survey, geophysical survey (the study of features below the Earth's surface) and fieldwalking. Artefacts (objects made by humans) and ecofacts (organic materials, such as seeds) can help us to understand the nature and impact of human activity. Britain is in archaeological terms one of the most thoroughly researched provinces of the empire. While archaeological evidence also has its limitations (for example, survival depends on the nature of the material, and inorganic materials are far more likely to survive than organic), it comes from every level of society.

Archaeologists investigate all aspects of people's lives, including topics which concern us today, such as conflict, social inequality, multiculturalism, migration, diet, disease and death. Archaeological evidence enables us to understand the challenges that faced people like us, and how they coped. It is an amazing story of endurance, resilience, ingenuity and creativity, often in the face of immense social and political upheaval. The importance of material remains as a source of information about past societies has been recognised by scholars and antiquarians (precursors to modern archaeologists) for hundreds of years.

Ancient sources are also important in this period, as the Roman invasion of Britain traditionally marks the transition from the prehistoric to the historical period. However, archaeological evidence is particularly valuable because textual sources are sparser than for other periods, such as medieval and Tudor England.

Through a combination of narrative and recent archaeological research, this book explores the nature of everyday life under Roman rule. The narrative imagines the experiences and responses of ordinary people over four centuries, and has been inspired by recent archaeological discoveries in Leicester. Leicester (*Ratae Corieltavorum*) is examined in detail because it is one of the most excavated urban centres in Britain, and the range of evidence shows us that it was a vibrant multicultural centre from its earliest phases.

Right: Kathleen Kenyon's excavations of the Jewry Wall Roman baths in Leicester in the 1930s as recorded by the artist Alan Sorrell. This was his first sketch of an archaeological excavation; he went on to become a famous archaeological illustrator. Archaeologists first interpreted these structures as the town's forum (town square and town hall). Illustrated London News, 13 Feb. 1937. Credit: Alan Sorrell. Courtesy of the estate of Alan Sorrell

LEICESTER'S ROMAN FORUM TO-DAY: A CITY'S UNIQUE HERITAGE.

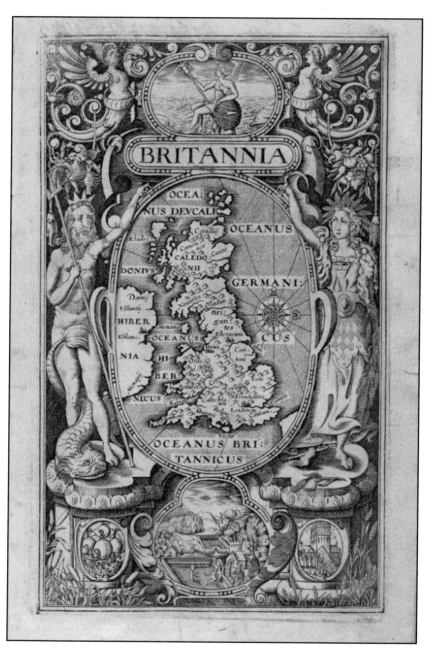

Above: Frontispiece of the 1607 edition of William Camden's Britannia.
Credit: Wellcome Collection

Britain in the Roman world: ancient sources

Britain was under Roman rule for nearly four centuries. Unfortunately, there are very few written sources, and those we do have are problematic because they were primarily written by wealthy, educated, elite males living outside Britain. They were also aimed at an educated elite in Rome, and therefore are of limited value for understanding the lives of ordinary people. The account by Julius Caesar of his campaigns in Britain and Gaul was important in shaping his public image in Rome in a period of intense political rivalry. While his writing provides important insights into life in Britain in this period, he was largely writing to promote his achievements at home and it is therefore important to assess his account alongside other forms of evidence.

Tacitus' *Agricola* (AD 98) is another important source for Roman Britain. *Agricola* is a panegyric (a text or speech which praises someone) and was written by Tacitus to celebrate the achievements of his father-in-law, a renowned governor of Britain. Unfortunately, Tacitus rarely mentions place or tribe names because he was writing for an aristocratic audience in Rome that had little interest in such a remote and 'barbarous' place. It is therefore very difficult for archaeologists and historians to reconstruct the events he describes. He makes only limited references to the achievements of Agricola's predecessors as governor, because the work was written to honour Agricola.

Other important sources include the writing of Cassius Dio (c. AD 220), a Roman statesman and historian, and itineraries and road maps such as the *Antonine Itinerary*. The *Itinerary* was compiled in the 3rd century, and records 225 roads across the empire, including 15 routes and over 100 place-names for Britain including Leicester.

In all the sources, a key theme is the difference between the 'barbarous' Britons and the 'civilised' Romans, with stereotypical images of the Britons as semi-clothed savages, subsisting in inhospitable landscapes. They served to bolster the Roman view that civilisation declined with distance from Rome. However, this stereotypical image of the British is in many respects unsupported by the archaeological evidence.

Epigraphy (inscriptions), for example on tomb stones, and finds such as the curse tablets from Leicester (*Ratae Corieltavorum*) and Bath (*Aquae Sulis*), provide rare and important insights into the lives of ordinary people living in Roman Britain.

Excavating the classical world: the 18th century

In the eighteenth and nineteenth centuries there was intense rivalry between Britain and other European nations (particularly France) to lay claim to the classical (Greek and Roman) world. European nations saw themselves as successors to the great classical civilisations, and huge effort was invested in excavating and recording archaeological sites and antiquities.

The rigorous study of Greek and Roman literature and language was an essential part of an aristocratic (male) education and an important marker of social status from at least the sixteenth century. A Grand Tour of Europe was an important element of this classical education. Many impressive collections of classical antiquities were established in this period as aristocrats returned home with sculptures and vases to adorn their stately homes.

This enthusiasm for classical art and architecture was fuelled by the discovery and excavation in Italy of the Roman towns of Pompeii and Herculaneum (preserved by the eruption of Mount Vesuvius in AD 79) in the early eighteenth century. The excavations attracted huge interest throughout Europe and beyond, and the towns became an important destination for those undertaking a tour of Europe.

Classical art and architecture served as a source of inspiration for writers, artists, architects, and interior designers. For example, Holkham Hall in Norfolk was built between 1734 and 1764 by the politician and agricultural reformer Thomas Coke, later earl of Leicester. His interest in classical art and architecture was inspired by his six-year Grand Tour of Europe. He returned to Norfolk in 1718, bringing with him works of art, many of which are still on display in the Hall today.

Holkham Hall itself is built in the Palladian style; this style is based on the designs of the 16th-century Italian architect Andrea Palladio (1508–80), who was himself inspired by the buildings of ancient Rome.

Antiquarians were keen to find and catalogue inscriptions and coins which served to illustrate the stories told by ancient authors. Antiquarians also documented standing Roman remains. The famous antiquary William Stukeley recorded the Jewry Wall baths in Leicester, which he interpreted as a temple of Janus (below).

The study of Roman military history was also important in this period. William Roy's book *The Military Antiquities of the Romans in Britain* (1793) was widely read (Roy later founded the Ordnance Survey, a national mapping agency in Britain). Britain's empire was rapidly expanding in this period and the Romans were greatly admired for their administrative and military prowess.

Above: Excavation of the Temple of Isis in Pompeii. *Coloured etching by Pietro Fabris, 1776. Credit: Wellcome Collection*

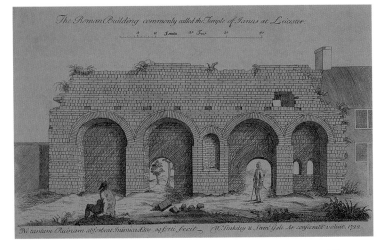

Above: Drawing of the Jewry Wall by the famous antiquary William Stukeley, published in his Itinerarium Curiosum *(1722). Credit: Special Collections, University of Leicester*

Right: The mosaics discovered at Woodchester were painstakingly recorded by Samuel Lysons (1797), working with leading artists and scientists of the day. The Orpheus mosaic is the largest mosaic discovered in Britain. Photograph by Colin Brooks. Credit: Special Collections, University of Leicester

Below: The Roman villa at Bignor (Sussex) (1817). Excavated by John Hawkins and Samuel Lysons. Photograph by Colin Brooks. Credit: Special Collections, University of Leicester

In the 18th century there was widespread acceptance of the idea that Britain had been a military outpost and cultural backwater on the edge of the Roman Empire. However, by the end of the 18th century archaeological discoveries suggested otherwise. As impressive villas and mosaics were accidentally discovered by farm labourers, such as those at Woodchester (Gloucestershire) and Bignor (Sussex), enthusiastic and talented antiquarians set about exploring and interpreting these discoveries. They helped to demonstrate that Britain had been fully part of the Roman world, with art and architecture to rival those found elsewhere in the empire.

Excavating Roman Britain: 18th and 19th centuries

Samuel Lysons' excavations at Woodchester (Gloucestershire) and Bignor (Sussex) were two of the earliest systematic excavations in Britain. He worked with an eminent group of scientists and artists to accurately record these and other Roman villa sites, and their publications are still used by archaeologists today.

Romano-British towns, villas, mosaics and baths were believed to be important indicators of civilisation. Many local archaeological and historical societies were established in the nineteenth century, such as the Leicestershire Architectural and Archaeological Society, and their members enthusiastically explored and debated these discoveries. Archaeology became an important pastime for the middle classes. The excavations of the Roman forts at Lympne (Kent) and Pevensey (Sussex) in the 1850s attracted hundreds of visitors. One of the archaeologists, Charles Roach Smith (1807–90), was presented with a free pass from the London and South East Railway Company because the company recognised that the 'excavations attracted hundreds weekly; and that it was in their interest to encourage them'.

Charles Roach Smith also collected thousands of Roman artefacts from London, many of which were discovered accidentally during construction projects, including the digging of tunnels for the City's sewers. They were displayed in his Museum of London Antiquities which became an important visitor attraction. After a huge and lengthy campaign Roach Smith and many other leading archaeologists of the day persuaded the British Museum to purchase his collection for the nation, and it formed the basis of the Romano-British gallery in the British Museum.

While most histories of archaeology focus on the exploits of men, and women were largely excluded from the membership of national and local archaeological societies, they nevertheless made a huge contribution to the development of archaeology in this period. They often played an important role in recording archaeological discoveries (many were talented artists), organised meetings and events, and helped to establish and curate museum collections. Anna Gurney (1795–1857) was the first female member of the British Archaeological Society. She was a renowned scholar of Old English and a keen supporter of archaeological projects. In addition to her scholarly achievements, she was well known for her many and varied charitable activities, including support for the emancipation of slaves and for the education and welfare of poor children. More than 2,000 people attended her funeral near Cromer in Norfolk.

CHARLES ROACH SMITH.
FROM THE MARBLE BY
SIGNOR FONTANA.

PRESENTED BY JOSEPH MAYER.

Top right: Charles Roach Smith, Frontispiece, Charles Roach Smith: Retrospections, Social and Archaeological, *Volume 1 (1883). London: Printed by subscription*

Bottom right: Photograph of Anna Gurney, first female member of the British Archaeological Association. Credit: Norfolk Museums Service (Norwich Castle Museum & Art Gallery)

Archaeology and imperialism

The admiration for Roman military prowess, and the trappings of Roman elite culture, was fuelled in part by the importance of a traditional classical education, but also by a widespread belief in the benefits of empire. This enthusiasm for empire and imperialism reached a peak in the 19th century, which is perhaps unsurprising given that between 1815 and 1914 400 million people came under British rule. By the end of the 19th century Britain ruled one-third of the territory and population of the world! The structure and administration of Britain's empire were in part modelled on that of the Roman Empire. The views of the archaeologist Francis Haverfield, writing in the early 20th century, show the sympathy of Roman archaeologists with modern colonialism: 'whatever their limitations, the men of the [Roman] Empire wrought for the betterment and happiness of the world'. The concept of Romanisation, which was believed to be an inevitable and generally beneficial process resulting in the adoption of a Roman way of life, underpinned Roman archaeology throughout most of the 20th century.

Today, archaeologists of Roman Britain are understandably less sympathetic to these ideas, and are instead concerned with understanding the diverse, or discrepant, experiences of all people living under Roman rule. In the 21st century there has been considerable debate about the nature and impact of Roman rule in Britain, fuelled by the rapidly expanding body of archaeological evidence. It is now recognised that local traditions were not always abandoned in favour of new 'Roman' forms, such as Roman-style houses and public buildings; instead the situation was far more complex, with an infinite variety of individual, local and regional responses to Roman rule across the empire.

Above: Statue of George I in Roman attire by Michael Rysbrack (Cambridge University Library, Cambridge). Credit: David Bridgwater, Fitzwilliam Museum and Cambridge University Library, with permission

The Diana and bull sculpture (above), from the villa at Woodchester, Gloucestershire. The reconstruction by the renowned sculptor John Flaxman (1755–1826) is illustrated alongside the original (Woodchester 1797, plate XXXVIII). The discovery of high-quality sculpture attracted great interest and excitement in this period because it showed that Britain had Roman artwork which rivalled that found in Italy. Photograph by Colin Brooks. *Credit: Special Collections, University of Leicester.*

Plate VI. Fig. 2 p. 10.

Mosaic Pavement at M.r Worthington's in Leicester.

From a Drawing taken by M.r Carter. 1788, & now in the Library of the Society of Antiquaries.

J. Carter del.

J. Schnebbelie sculp.

Antiquarians and archaeologists have been interested in Leicest past for hundreds of years. Medieval chroniclers connected Roman ruins still visible in the town with the mythical K Lear (later of Shakespearean fame). By the seventeenth centu antiquarians like William Burton (1622) were describing the f archaeological discoveries—coins, pottery and mosaics.

Burton was one of the first people to link Leicester with the Rom settlement of *Ratae*, first mentioned by Ptolemy (a mathematici scientist and geographer of the 2nd century AD). Bur unequivocally located *Ratae* within the Roman Empire.

One of the earliest Roman mosaics recorded in Britain was fou near All Saints' Church on Highcross Street in 1675. It depi the story of Cyparissus and his pet stag. In a version of the my Cyparissus accidentally kills the stag and Apollo transforms inconsolable boy into a cypress tree, a symbol of mourning still fou in many cemeteries today. This is the only known representation Cyparissus in Britain.

The Leicestershire Architectural & Archaeological Society (now Leicestershire Archaeological & Historical Society) was found in 1855 'to promote the study of ecclesiastical, general antiquit and the restoration of mutilated architectural remains within county'. James Thompson, one of the founders of the Soci was proprietor of the *Leicester Chronicle*, later the *Leicester D Mercury*, and was a leading authority on the history of Leices In 1849 he published a *History of Leicester* from the time of Romans to the end of the 17th century. Thompson was also honorary curator of the Leicester Museum. He contributed arti on Roman and Anglo-Saxon Antiquities and the Jewry Wall to first volume of the *Transactions of the Leicestershire Architect and Archaeological Society*, and corresponded regularly with fel antiquarians across Britain, including Charles Roach Sm Many of these early archaeologists were middle-class profession including members of the clergy, doctors, wealthy merchants industrialists, working tirelessly in their free time to study, rec and publish archaeological discoveries. They played an import role in establishing Archaeology as a scientific discipline.

Left: The Cyparissus Pavement*, Nichols 1795. Credit: Special Collections, University of Leicester*

Uncovering Roman Leicester: Kathleen Kenyon

Dame Kathleen Kenyon (1906–78) was a pioneering archaeologist who made an important contribution to our understanding of Roman Leicester when she excavated the Jewry Wall Roman baths in the 1930s (see photographs opposite). She was the first female president of the Oxford Archaeological Society, and was Principal of St Hugh's College, Oxford (1962–73). Kenyon is best known for her excavations at Tell as-Sultān in Jordan, the site of Old Testament Jericho, but first established a reputation as a meticulous field archaeologist through her excavations at many British sites, including *Verulamium* (St Albans) and *Ratae* (Leicester). Her excavations at Leicester were the first large-scale archaeological investigation of the Roman town and paved the way for eighty years of archaeological discoveries in the city.

At 23 m long, 9 m high and 2.5 m thick, the Jewry Wall is one of the largest pieces of Roman masonry still standing in Britain. Since the medieval period, when it was commonly believed to be part of the Roman town gate (*janua*) or a Temple to Janus, there was much discussion about what the Jewry Wall may have been. It was not until it was excavated in the late 1930s by Kenyon (coincidentally in preparation for the building of a new public swimming baths) that its role as part of a substantial bathing complex was demonstrated, showing that it was not the town's forum as previously thought.

Why is Leicester's Roman bath complex known as the Jewry Wall? There are several theories. The name dates back to at least the 17th century and may be a misspelling of the latin *janua* (meaning gateway) or the Roman god Janus. Both words were linked with the monument in the medieval period. Another theory is that this area of Leicester was once a Jewish quarter, as early spellings of the name sometimes refer to it as the 'Jews Wall'. Alternatively, it may have come from the word 'jury', referring to meetings of the medieval borough's councillors (or 'jurats') who may have gathered in St Nicholas' churchyard next to the wall.

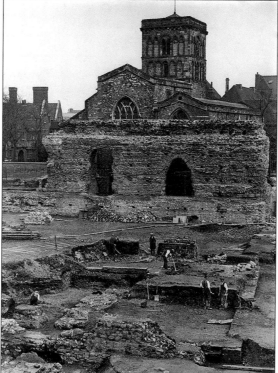

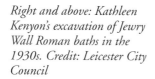

Right and above: Kathleen Kenyon's excavation of Jewry Wall Roman baths in the 1930s. Credit: Leicester City Council

Uncovering Roman Leicester: recent excavations

Further excavations were carried out in Leicester by Jean Mellor and the Leicestershire Archaeological Unit (LAU), who excavated many sites in the 1960s, '70s and '80s, including the Roman forum (today beneath Jubilee Square) and Leicester's only known Roman temple, a *mithraeum*, dedicated to the god Mithras (today beneath St Nicholas Circle).

From the mid-1990s, LAU's successor University of Leicester Archaeological Services (ULAS) has carried out major programmes of excavation in the city. One of the largest excavations took place between 2003 and 2006 when the former Shires Shopping Centre was extended into the Highcross retail quarter. It was clear that archaeological remains would be damaged by the foundations of the new buildings, so these were carefully investigated to create a detailed record. Excavations took place at Vine Street (now beneath the John Lewis car park); Vaughan Way, and along Highcross Street (see map). The remains of 40 Roman buildings, including town houses, shops and workshops, a warehouse and a small bath house, were uncovered.

In 2016–17 excavations were carried out by ULAS on the former Stibbe factory site, between Great Central Street and Highcross Street in central Leicester. Key discoveries include pieces of one of the largest and highest-status Roman mosaic floors ever found in the city, two Roman streets containing a number of buildings including part of a theatre (a first for Leicester) and rare evidence of the first Anglo-Saxon migrants to arrive in the city in the 5th and 6th centuries.

The thousands of finds from the excavations were analysed by specialists at ULAS to gain a better understanding of the lives of the city's past inhabitants. As you will see, the remains of buildings, artefacts and ecofacts allow us to

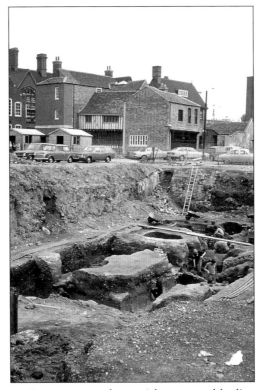

investigate aspects such as social status, wealth, diet, health and religious beliefs and practices. Through the analysis of these discoveries, archaeologists have constructed a detailed picture of how Leicester might have looked from the earliest phases of its development in the pre-Roman era through to the present day.

Top left: Excavating Leicester's Roman forum in the 1970s (today beneath Jubilee Square). Credit: ULAS

Top right: Excavating a Roman mosaic at the former Stibbe factory site in Leicester in 2017. Credit: ULAS

Left: The handle of a folding Roman clasp knife in the shape of a dog, found at Vine Street. Credit: ULAS

So far, archaeologists have excavated about 11% of Leicester, making it one of the most extensively investigated Roman cities in Britain.

The Village

Call me Maglus. Call me Mars, Mercury, Neptune or Silvanus. Call me as you wish. I'm a god with many names. And before, hundreds of years ago, when this land was young and still one thing with the Continent, I had no name. You humans have a thing for names. Birds and deer worshipped me long before you came, and yet they didn't have a name for me.

I've always lived here, near the ford. I now live with you, in this bunch of houses made of wood and mud that you call home. Now, the air smells of woodsmoke and manure in winter and wet clay in summer. I don't care much. Give me milk when it's cold and blood when it's hot and I'm content.

Some of you praise me very much. Take this young boy, Senedo. He made a tiny portrait of me, carved in the shinbone of a lamb. He lives with his family in one of the roundhouses near the river. I go and visit them sometimes. His mother, Vorvena, is tall and blonde, with dark eyes and thin hands. His younger sister, Cocca, is quiet and smells of grass and whey. His father is old and grouchy and never told me his name. I like to sit with them in front of the fire that crackles in the middle of the house, the smoke coiling up into the thatched roof.

Vorvena is good at telling stories. She sometimes talks about the people that came from overseas, years ago, with shiny armour and horsehair on their heads. They landed south, where the white cliffs are. She says the grandfather of her father saw them. I saw them too.

It was late summer, cold winds already blowing from the sea. At dawn, a large fleet of ships, of different size and shape, appeared in the distance. I was not alone on the cliffs. Hundreds of men were scanning the horizon with me. I heard their agitated voices. I heard them banging their swords on their shields to shake off the fear. I had my sword and shield, too.

The invaders called themselves Romans. Their leader, Caesar, was a short man with deep-set eyes and little hair. He was brusque and sharp and talked very little. Good general, though. We fought his soldiers on the shore. When we were close to pushing them back, they started hurling bolts of iron from their ships. I saw a man at my side thrown into the air by one of them. He was dead before he hit the ground a couple of strides away.

Vorvena says that the invaders will return. Senedo is not afraid; he says he will fight them back. I believe him. He is only eleven but knows how to ride and soon will learn how to fight. In the penumbra of the room, I often catch him glancing at his father's sword, the hilt glaring in a corner.

One chilly night, Senedo's father falls asleep and never wakes up. Early in the morning, I see Senedo and his uncles carrying the body outside. His eyes are dry. They carry the body into the woods, followed by a small group of people. Nobody says a word. They will place the old man carefully under an oak tree, where birds, foxes, and worms will claim him back to the earth.

In the evening, the boy comes to my place. He pours a bowl of milk in the flow and calls my name. He's crying softly, now.

Leicester before the Romans (100 BC–AD 43)

In the late Iron Age the people known as the *Corieltavi* lived a largely rural life. The *Corieltavi* predominantly inhabited family-sized farms and small village-like settlements. Archaeological evidence shows that they were well networked with Gaul (France) and the wider Roman world.

The *Corieltavi* were not a single cohesive group with one leader but were a loose amalgamation of smaller groups with local leaders held together by networks of allegiance and family loyalties. They occupied much of Leicestershire, Rutland, Lincolnshire, and parts of Derbyshire, Nottinghamshire and Northamptonshire. The large pre-Roman settlements at Leicester, Lincoln and Sleaford (Lincolnshire) were important centres for some of the groups. The Romans recorded Leicester's name as *Ratae*, which means 'ramparts', implying that a sizeable defended settlement existed at this time.

The remains of this first settlement at Leicester have been found on the east bank of the River Soar (near St Nicholas Circle in the modern city), where there are traces of roundhouses, pits and ditches covering an area of approximately 10 hectares. Objects from this early settlement suggest that *Ratae* was a high-status site with connections with the rest of Britain and

the Continent. Archaeological discoveries included high-quality pottery imports from Gaul, Italy and Spain. There is also evidence for coin production in the form of clay trays which were used to create coin blanks. Portions of metal were placed in the holes in these trays and then in a furnace for melting. The pellets were then hammered until they were flat and struck between two dies (carrying images) to create a coin. Examples of these trays from Bath Lane in Leicester show that the settlement had a mint from the late 1st century BC.

The *Corieltavi* were the most northerly British people to produce coins in the Iron Age. The earliest coins local to Leicester were found at Hallaton and had no writing on them. From the 1st century AD coins were inscribed. The lettering on these coins is some of the earliest evidence of writing in Britain. The people who ordered the minting of the coins must have had considerable power and authority and were familiar with developments in the Roman world.

Below: Iron Age Leicester as it may have looked from the south during the early 1st century AD. Credit: Sarah Greeves / ULAS

Left: Part of a clay tray used to melt metal in order to create blanks for making coins, and a silver coin of the Corieltavi (1st century AD) depicting a stylised horse. Credit: ULAS

Caesar's invasions of Britain (55 and 54 BC)

In the late Roman Republic, during the last century BC when Rome and Britain had their first violent encounter, there was no single political figurehead in Rome. Instead, a large and highly competitive political elite fought tooth and nail for their own advantage. Julius Caesar was a key player in the last days of the Republic, and his leadership of military campaigns in the provinces afforded opportunities for both financial enrichment and military glory.

Julius Caesar first invaded Britain on 23 August 55 BC. His army, which was around 10,000 strong, did not venture further than Kent, but his exploits attracted huge attention in Rome because Britain lay beyond the world known to the Romans. Caesar's invasion of Britain was part of a far larger campaign, which included a nine-year battle for Gaul between 58 and 51 BC. The key source of information about his exploits is Caesar's own written account *De bello Gallico*, in which he describes his campaign across modern France, Belgium and Switzerland, which included crossing both the river Rhine and the sea (the English Channel) which was believed to encompass the Roman world.

Caesar returned to Britain in 54 BC in response to a request for protection from Mandubracius, a prince of the Iron Age tribe the *Trinobantes*. The Roman army campaigned through the area encompassing modern Kent, Greater London, Hertfordshire and Essex, before winning a decisive victory that ensured the safety of the *Trinobantes*. As part of the peace settlement, which Caesar secured by the taking of hostages, the tribes of south-east England were required to pay tribute to Rome.

Above: Caesar's invasion of Britain by Edward Armitage (c. 1843). Credit: Wellcome Collection

Julius Caesar does not tell us exactly where his army landed in 54 BC, saying only that it was 'the best place of disembarkation'. He does, however, give three important topographical clues (descriptions of physical features) to its whereabouts.

1. In order for the army to embark and disembark in daylight, the Roman fleet set sail from France in the evening and sailed through the night. The plan was to use the wind to help them cross the Channel, but around midnight the wind dropped and the tide carried the fleet too far north. At sunrise they saw Britain a long way away on the port (left) side. This must be the east coast of Kent, if the tide had carried them west, the British coast would have been on the starboard (right) side.

2. Caesar wrote that the Britons had gathered to oppose the landing. But taken aback by the size of the Roman fleet—800 ships—they withdrew 'and concealed themselves on the high ground'. This matches the high ground and cliffs of the North Downs to the south, or the Isle of Thanet to the north.

3. In separate passages, Caesar described the landing place as being the best place to land and that it had a soft or sandy, open shore. This description is consistent with Pegwell Bay, which today is the largest bay on the east Kent coast and is open and flat. The bay is big enough for the whole Roman army to have landed in the single day that Caesar describes.

In Caesar's footsteps

Above: View of the excavations at Ebbsfleet in 2016 showing Pegwell Bay and the cliffs at Ramsgate in the background. Credit: Dean Barkley

Recent research carried out by University of Leicester archaeologists suggest that in 54 BC Caesar's fleet landed in Pegwell Bay on the Isle of Thanet in north-east Kent and constructed a fort nearby. This location matches Caesar's own account of his landing, with three clues about the physical features of the landing site being consistent with him having landed in Pegwell Bay: its visibility from the sea, the existence of a large open bay, and the presence of higher ground nearby.

The project involved surveys of hillforts that may have been attacked by Caesar, studies in museums of objects that may have been made or buried at the time of the invasions, such as coin hoards, and excavations in Kent.

Excitingly, the shape of a large defensive ditch at Ebbsfleet, a hamlet between Ramsgate and Sandwich, is very similar to some of the Roman defences at Alesia in France, where the decisive battle in the Gallic War (Caesar's campaign against the Gauls) took place in 52 BC.

The site overlooks Pegwell Bay and is now 900 m inland but at the time of Caesar's invasions it was closer to the coast. The ditch is 5 m wide and 2 m deep, and is dated by pottery and radiocarbon dates to the 1st century BC. The size, shape and date of the defences at Ebbsfleet, and the presence of iron weapons including a Roman *pilum* (javelin), all suggest that Ebbsfleet was a Roman base in the 1st century BC. The site, up to 20 hectares in size, was probably used as a fort to protect the ships of Caesar's fleet which would have been drawn up on a nearby beach.

Above left: View of the defensive ditch at Ebbsfleet. Credit: University of Leicester
Above right: A Roman pilum tip from Ebbsfleet, found in the ditch. Credit: University of Leicester

Leicestershire at the time of the invasion (AD 43)

The discovery of an open-air hilltop shrine at Hallaton in south-east Leicestershire offers a new understanding of the Iron Age to Roman transition in this region. Previously archaeologists assumed that before the invasion of AD 43, Roman diplomatic contacts extended only as far as south-east England. However, a Roman helmet found at the site is thought to have been a diplomatic gift. Negotiations with the imperial authorities before or during the conquest would help explain the choice of the nearby settlement at *Ratae* (Leicester) as the capital of the self-governing civitas of the *Corieltavi* within the developing imperial province. The nature of the deposits suggests it was the location of communal rituals organised by elites of the *Corieltavi*. A settlement with roundhouses in a ditched enclosure was located close by to the north of the shrine, and pottery suggests that these were occupied in the 1st century AD.

The activities at the shrine on the hill involved feasting on sacrificed pigs; archaeologists found pig bones buried by the entrance. The rites also included the deliberate burial of several hoards of metalwork in pits. These hoards contained coins, but also other objects, such as a unique silver bowl and items of military equipment. The coins included 350 Roman examples, and more than 5,000 Iron Age British ones. Especially surprising was the burial of a Roman cavalry helmet (below left), plus the cheek-pieces from several others, all with silver decoration. The Hallaton bowl (below middle) is possibly the earliest known example of a silver object made by a native Briton. The bowl may have been used in ritual ceremonies prior to its burial; it sits easily in the hand and is ideally suited for drinking from.

Some of the Roman coins in the hoard were of a type called *denarii*, many of which were already more than 100 years old when they were buried. The oldest *denarius* found at Hallaton probably dates from 211 BC (below right), making it one of the oldest Roman coins found in Britain (it was struck in Rome before the Roman general Scipio defeated Hannibal in the Second Punic War between Rome and Carthage). These coins show that there was long-distance trade and diplomacy between Leicestershire and Rome before the Roman conquest.

Above: The reconstructed cavalry helmet from Hallaton is now on display in Harborough Museum, Market Harborough. Credit: © Leicestershire County Council

Above: The Hallaton silver bowl. Senedo may have used something similar when he poured a devotional offer of milk into the river (see page 14)

Above: The oldest Roman coin in Britain? It shows the goddess Roma on one side and the twins Castor and Pollox on galloping horses on the reverse. Credit: © Leicestershire County Council

War

War is on us. The wind smells of fire, tells me stories of sacred groves reduced to ashes, of shamans slaughtered on holy ground. Stories of prodigious, armoured beasts ridden by wicked tamers. Stories of proud kings kneeling in front of a lame man. Over and over again, I see bands of men retreating north, messily. Their feet bleeding, the hair on their forehead stuck down with sweat. 'They have crossed the great river', they say, 'they'll be here before midwinter'.

Senedo left last summer, aiming south with ten companions. They left at night, against the will of the elders. They disappeared like ghosts, swallowed by darkness. That night, Cocca came to me. She implored me to go with her brother and protect him in battle, like I had done with her ancestors. 'He's only sixteen'. She said that because she was scared, but knew already I wouldn't go. Senedo has grown reckless and arrogant and doesn't want my help. He insulted his uncle when he tried to reason with him. He can't think of anything but war. It's not about fighting the invaders. It's war itself that lures him. I've seen men much wiser than he is touched by this disease and none of them ever recovered. Nothing I can do to change that.

Days pass by, midwinter comes and goes. Then, on a morning of pale spring, the Romans come, hundreds of them. They march north: infantry first, their armour stained with mud and blood; the horsemen follow, shiny and bold. The village stays still, the air full of the harsh clang of their shields and the whinnies of their horses. I look at them, at their weary faces, their fancy helmets, their short spears. Some are small and swarthy, with sturdy legs and long, thin noses. Some are tall and fair, with bluish tattoos and red moustaches.

And then I see him. A young horseman, a grand helmet shading his face, his eyes bright with pride. Suddenly, he whispers something to the man riding at his side and tightens the reins. I watch him leaving the group, trotting towards the house near the ford. He dismounts. Vorvena and Cocca are on the doorstep, the mother shielding her daughter, their eyes wide open. Vorvena holds a knife in her hand. The young man removes his helmet. Nobody says a word. He didn't need my help, after all.

Claudius' invasion of Britain (AD 43)

Claudius, Emperor of Rome. Line engraving, after A. Sadeler after Titian. Credit: Wellcome Collection

Throughout the course of his political career, Caesar's great-nephew and heir, Octavian, gradually undermined Rome's long-cherished Republican principles to create a hereditary monarchy, becoming the first emperor, known as Augustus. He dramatically reformed Rome's political and administrative structures, doubled the size of the provincial empire and constructed an elaborate personality cult around himself and his family. He was ruthless and ambitious.

After Caesar's famous exploits in Britain, the possibility of invasion was considered by Augustus, and then by later emperors Caligula and Claudius, who were all keen to emulate Caesar's achievements. Military victories remained an essential requirement for political success in the empire.

Claudius' invasion in AD 43 was under the command of the general Aulus Plautius. The army included approximately 20,000 men based around four legions, and roughly the same number in auxiliary units (cavalry and infantry recruited from conquered peoples to support the citizen legions).

The exact details of the landing are unclear, but the main aim was to cross the Thames and to march to Colchester (*Camulodunum*), which was the seat of an important British ruler. There was initially little opposition to the landing, but the Roman army eventually encountered a substantial British force at an unidentified river crossing, which resulted in a two-day battle. The army then advanced to the Thames and successfully secured a river crossing after a second battle. According to Dio's account, Plautius then sent word for Claudius to join him and the emperor arrived with a detachment of elephants, taking part in the siege and capture of Colchester. The spectacle of the elephants must have terrified the people of Britain, which may have been rather like witnessing an alien invasion!

On his carefully staged sixteen-day tour of Britain, Claudius took part in a series of battles and witnessed the surrender of several British leaders; an inscription on an arch in Rome describes the surrender of British kings to Claudius. Some of these were subsequently recognised as independent leaders by Rome to encourage cooperation. The Roman invasion force was then probably broken up into smaller units to continue the process of subjugation. *Legio XX* remained in Colchester to control the *Trinovantes*. *XIV Gemina* and *IX Hispana* were responsible for extending Roman control to the west, north and north-west, which included the region occupied by the *Corieltavi* in the East Midlands, and the territory of the *Dobunni* in the south-west.

Vespasian (who later became emperor) campaigned in the south-west with *Legio II; Suetonius records thirty skirmishes which resulted in the submission of two tribes, at least twenty native settlements and the Isle of Wight. There is archaeological evidence for Roman warfare at Hod Hill in Dorset, in the territory of the *Durotriges*, where ballista bolts had been fired into the interior of the hillfort. Evidence of violent encounters has been found at other hillforts in southern England and Wales, including Maiden Castle, Cadbury Castle and Llanymynech.

Conquest: the campaign for Britain

The Romans had an uncompromising and ruthless approach to battle; those who rebelled or resisted were mercilessly slaughtered. This tactic was underpinned by the belief that they had divine sanction for an 'empire without limits'. They were often manipulative and deceitful in their dealings with other peoples, and achieved their aims through intimidation and the threat of force.

The prestige associated with the governorship of Britain was second only to that in Syria, because of the size of the army and the opportunities to demonstrate military prowess. However, the continued use of military force was not always practical or sustainable, and other strategies were required. The use of diplomacy was regularly employed to capitalise on military success. For example, in Britain some peoples were accorded formal recognition as client kingdoms, such as the *Iceni* under their king, Prasutagus, the *Brigantes*

Above: Roman legionaries of the 1st century AD (Ermine Street Guard re-enactment group) Credit: Simon James

under Cartimandua, and the kingdom of Togidubnus—broadly the territory of the *Atrebates* (see map).

The formal recognition by Rome of a series of 'client kings' in Britain before and after the conquest is a sign that the peoples of Britain were by no means primitive 'tribes'. However, these arrangements were not usually viewed as a long-term solution. In periods of conquest, such diplomatic manoeuvres were often a means of isolating enemies from potential allies.

The speed of the conquest of Britain was influenced by events taking place elsewhere in the empire. Soldiers were withdrawn from Britain on numerous occasions to take part in wars elsewhere. *Legio XIV Gemina* was withdrawn around AD 67 in preparation for a campaign in the Balkans against the Parthians. The seemingly mysterious disappearance of the Ninth Legion (*Legio IX*) may have also been the result of a strategic transfer to another part of the empire, rather than a catastrophic conflict.

The impact of the Roman invasion on the people of Britain was immense. Tacitus frequently uses the word 'terror' in relation to Agricola's campaigns in the north of Britain (AD 77–84). Intimidation and extreme force were characteristic, particularly when resistance was strong. The burning of villages and the destruction of crops were commonly used tactics for subjugating people. Many men were killed in battle, and women, children and the elderly were often subjected to massacres, enslavement, rape and displacement as refugees. Property and land were frequently seized in the aftermath of a battle. Based on descriptions in the sources, and what we know about the nature of ancient warfare, it is estimated that somewhere between 100,000 and 250,000 out of a population of approximately 2 million Britons were killed between AD 43 and 83 as the Romans slowly conquered their new province.

Above: The Roman conquest of Britain, AD 43–84

Newly conquered people were often recruited by the Roman army as auxiliary soldiers. This strategy helped to prevent further resistance, while strengthening Rome's military capacity. Two cavalry units (*alae*) and at least sixteen infantry or mixed units (*cohortes*) were established in Britain through the recruitment of defeated peoples. Defeated communities were required to pay tribute, and to provide forced labour and animals. Leicester was no exception. From a bronze military diploma found in the Roman city of Porolissum (in northern Romania), we know that at least one of Leicester's residents, a man called Marcus Ulpius Novantico (the son of Adcobrovatus of *Ratae*), joined the First Cohort of Britains in the late 1st century AD and fought during the Emperor Trajan's Dacian Wars (AD 101–6). He gained Roman citizenship for distinguished service in AD 106 and was discharged from the army in 110. A thousand miles from home, there is no evidence he returned to Leicester.

The army adopted a highly structured approach to military campaigning, usually marching between 10 and 20 miles each day, followed by a night spent in a temporary and defensible camp. These camps provide evidence for the Roman campaigns in Britain and have been found as far north as the Scottish Highlands. While it is often difficult to date these sites, the largest are over 40 hectares (100 acres) in size and could have accommodated up to approximately 50,000 men in tents.

In the five years following their invasion, the Roman army advanced northwards through the lands of the *Trinovantes*, the *Catuvellauni* and the *Corieltavi*. Fording the river Soar at Leicester, where they appear to have established a small fort to guard the crossing, the Fourteenth Legion (*Legio XIV Gemina*) established a fortress near Mancetter on the Leicestershire–Warwickshire border. Their route had probably taken them from Colchester north-west through Cambridgeshire and Northamptonshire and along the valley of the river Welland into Leicestershire, past Hallaton and on to Leicester. This route would later become a Roman road known today as the *Via Devana*. On a prominent flat hilltop overlooking the valley, 13 miles south-east of Leicester near the village of Weston by Welland, University of Leicester archaeologists have excavated part of a large but short-lived Roman marching camp. A deep ditch enclosed an area of at least 4 hectares in which traces of ephemeral structures, possibly tent positions, were found. This could have been a temporary base of the Fourteenth Legion as they advanced towards Leicester.

This methodical approach was adopted to lessen the risk of ambush or surprise attack. Training, uniforms, the routines of camp life, and so-called 'camp Latin' (*sermo militaris* or 'military talk') were essential for cohesion and operational flexibility. However, the army was far from monolithic, because it included men from increasingly diverse ethnic and social backgrounds. Men of senatorial rank might

Images of victory

Roman military equipment is frequently found in Britain, but the cavalry helmet from Hallaton is exceptional and one of the most elaborate examples of its kind from north-west Europe. The cheekpieces are decorated with scenes of Roman victory; the left with a cowering figure beneath a bare-headed rider, their hands on their head and an abandoned shield and helmet close by symbolising defeat. The rider is dressed in armour, with an arm outstretched in a salute, accompanied by a winged Victory holding aloft a victor's palm. The bowl of the helmet is decorated with a depiction of a laurel wreath and other symbols of victory including lions and their prey and a female bust, possibly Cybele the mother goddess, known in Roma as *Magna Mater* (Great Mother). The idea of war was central to Roman society, with great emphasis placed on the training, sacrifice and persistence required for success in battle.

The victorious rider is a Roman of high status; perhaps an emperor. There is debate as to whether the defeated figure is male or female. Some experts have suggested that the clothing indicates a woman; possibly making it one of the earliest depictions of 'Britannia', with her helmet and shield.

The helmet was probably a ceremonial object, worn only for special occasions rather than in battle, and may have been acquired by the *Corieltavi* before the Roman invasion; or perhaps it was a war trophy or was gifted to the *Corieltavi* by the Romans as they passed through the Midlands.

Above: The left cheekpiece from the Hallaton helmet. Credit: © Leicestershire County Council

Left: An artist's reconstruction of what the cavalry helmet from Hallaton may have looked like. Credit: Bob Whale © Leicestershire County Council

combine a political career in Rome with military service, perhaps beginning with a junior officer role and progressing to command of a legion. Such men often served in different legions and provinces at different times in their careers. Men of equestrian rank (wealthy landowners) might lead 500- or 1,000-strong auxiliary infantry cohorts and then rise to command cavalry units (there were approximately 12 such posts in Britain). Men of lower social ranks became centurions. Centurions were relatively well paid and might qualify for equestrian status on retirement. Below the centurions were the legionaries (soldiers), who enlisted for a period of 25 years, and had to be citizens under the age of 45. Auxiliary troops differed from the legionaries as they were non-citizens. Citizenship was awarded upon discharge, or occasionally to a whole unit for valour in battle. By the late 70s AD, in Britain, auxiliary soldiers outnumbered legionaries.

Resistance to Roman rule

There was understandably considerable resistance to the imposition of Roman rule in Britain. While the sources often describe the Romans as acting to defend themselves against unprovoked native attacks, it is far more likely that resistance and rebellion was a response to the aggression of the Roman army. Ostorius Scapula, who became governor in AD 47, disarmed peoples who had already submitted, including the client kingdoms. The *Iceni* in Norfolk had acquiesced to Roman rule without military confrontation but were then forcibly disarmed. The Iceni are reported to have rebelled, with some refusing to hand over their arms, but the resistance was quelled by Roman auxiliary units, and the *Iceni* kept their client status.

Caratacus, the son of the Catuvellaunian king Cunobelinus, reportedly led the resistance to the Roman invasion after the capture of Colchester. Forced westwards by the Romans, he led the *Silures*, and later the *Ordovices* in Wales in the 40s AD and was famous for his resistance to Rome, and for his persistence and resourcefulness in battle. He appears to have been championed as a war leader by peoples in western Britain after his escape from Colchester. After suffering defeats in south Wales, he moved northwards into the territory of the Ordovices, where he evaded capture once again, fleeing north-eastwards into Brigantian territory where he was taken prisoner by Queen Cartimandua and handed over to the Romans. He escaped execution because Claudius admired his resilience and valour in battle. Cassius Dio reports that he 'wandered about the city [of Rome] after his liberation; and after beholding its splendour and its magnitude he exclaimed: "And can you, then, who have got such possessions and so many of them, covet our poor tents?"' (Cassius Dio, *Roman History*).

Above: Caratacus at the Tribunal of Claudius at Rome. *Caratacus' bravery and fortitude are often romanticised in art and literature. Credit: Andrew Birrell (fl. 1782–1809), after Henry Fuseli (1741–1825) [Public domain], via Wikimedia Commons*

After the death of Claudius in AD 54, numerous uprisings and the cost of quelling them caused the emperor Nero to consider a withdrawal from Britain. However, the appointment of Quintus Veranius as governor in AD 57 marked the start of a new offensive against the *Silures* which appears to have been successful; they are not mentioned again in Roman sources. His successor Suetonius Paulinus successfully annexed Ordovician territory, and within three years of campaigning had reached the island of Anglesey (*Mona*). The Roman writer Tacitus describes the enemy lined up on the other side of the Menai Straits: cursing Druids, armed men and fanatical women. Suetonius Paulinus led the assault on Anglesey, massacring all those in his path and destroying the sacred groves.

Druids

The stereotypical image of Iron Age religion is of long-haired, cloaked figures with flowing robes, communing with the gods in forest groves. However, contemporary sources, such as Tacitus, convey an image of barbarous rituals, with 'groves consecrated to their savage cults: for they considered it a pious duty to slake the altars with captive blood and to consult their deities by means of human entrails' (Tacitus, *Annals* 14. 30).

While the accuracy of these sources is debatable, and undoubtedly exaggerated for dramatic effect, the Druids appear to have formed significant pockets of resistance to Roman rule. At the time of Caesar's invasion they wielded considerable social and political power, and were responsible for propagating religious lore. Iron Age shrines are known in Britain; some in southern Britain are associated with a timber building often surrounded by a *temenos* or sacred enclosure. However, Roman sources typically describe British deities as being worshipped in wild, natural places or in sacred woods or groves. This may explain why so few sites have been identified by archaeologists. Iron Age Britons were farmers for whom the cycles of the seasons, nature and the fertility of land and animals will have been hugely important.

While there is no specific evidence for Druids at Hallaton, the shrine appears to be a combination of the two types: an open-air shrine marked by a boundary ditch and palisade situated in a natural, open setting, but without any formal building. It had a clearly defined entrance, a boundary and areas for the burial of objects. Rituals included the burial of coins and metalwork on one side of the boundary, and the sacrifice of pigs and ritual feasting on the other. Fourteen coin hoards and the helmet hoard were buried over a period of 15–20 years, most likely indicating an annual celebration. The pigs were all killed at the same time of year, suggesting a festival in autumn or winter. The layout of the site also suggests that access may have been restricted to those presiding over the rituals and other ceremonial activities.

While Roman sources of the 1st century do not appear to regard the Druids as a serious threat, the drastic steps taken to subdue and then eradicate them in Britain and Gaul suggest otherwise. The Druids may have been targeted because they led a cultural resistance to the Romans through adherence to their native religion. Julius Caesar records that the Druids were held in great respect, acted as judges, and had the power to exclude people from religious festivals, making them social outcasts. In the run up to the assault on Anglesey, they probably encouraged resistance and revolt elsewhere in Britain. The need to pacify the rest of Britain and to reinvent British religion in 'Roman' form were therefore key priorities.

Tacitus and Cassius Dio both describe the revolts that took place in this period. Tacitus describes them as a *clades* (disaster), and while some exaggeration is likely, it is nonetheless clear that a bloodbath ensued.

Above: The stereotypical image of a British druid. Credit: Mike Codd

Above: Boadicea and Her Daughters, *by Thomas Thorneycroft (erected 1902); this statue is close to the Houses of Parliament in London. Credit: Mathew Morris*

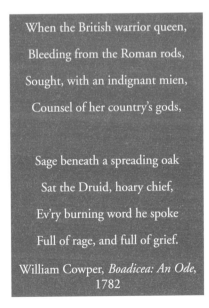

When the British warrior queen,

Bleeding from the Roman rods,

Sought, with an indignant mien,

Counsel of her country's gods,

Sage beneath a spreading oak

Sat the Druid, hoary chief,

Ev'ry burning word he spoke

Full of rage, and full of grief.

William Cowper, *Boadicea: An Ode,* 1782

Boudica

While Paulinus was fighting in Wales, the political situation in the rest of the province remained turbulent. In the aftermath of the Roman occupation much of the east of England was dominated by the *Iceni*. When the old king Prasutagus died his will stated that his wife Boudica and their daughters were to be co-heirs with the emperor. The Roman procurator Decianus Catus ignored the terms of the will, however, and mistreated the family, plundering their property (Tacitus, *Annals* 14. 31). When the surviving members of the royal family complained at the treatment of their people, Boudica was flogged and her daughters raped. The arrogance and corruption of the Roman administration provoked full-scale revolt. Boudica led the *Iceni* in rebellion, and other tribes outraged by Roman arrogance and cruelty, enthusiastically supported the revolt. The *Trinovantes* were particularly keen to join the rebellion, as many had been expelled from their lands to make way for Roman veteran colonists (retired Roman soldiers) based at *Camulodunum* (Colchester). Cassius Dio explains the severity of the rebellion, claiming that the Roman procurator demanded the return of the financial gifts that Claudius had bestowed on many leading Britons. He also records that in the early years of the province, Seneca (adviser to the emperor Nero), had attempted to make a profit from the new province by forcing the Britons to accept enormous loans. He later recalled these loans earning the hostility of many leading Britons (Dio, *Roman History* 62. 2. 1).

The Romans were unprepared for the speed with which much of Britain broke out in rebellion. Boudica rampaged through the province. The newly established, and strategically important, Roman settlements at *Camulodunum* (Colchester), *Londinium* (London) and *Verulamium* (St Albans) were sacked and their Roman inhabitants killed. The attack on *Camulodunum* was a carefully planned assault on a symbolically important settlement; the great temple dedicated to the divine Claudius, the ultimate sign of Rome's political and religious authority over Britain, was destroyed. The cult of Claudius was unpopular in Britain because the expenses related to the service of the cult were bankrupting local aristocracies (Tacitus, *Annals* 14. 31).

Paulinus struggled to bring the rebellion under control and was forced to abandon the city of *Londinium* (Tacitus, *Annals*. 14. 33). Eventually he assembled an army of around 10,000 men to face the much larger British force in a pitched battle located somewhere in the Midlands (High Cross and Mancetter on the Leicestershire–Warwickshire border are two of many suggested locations). In this kind of pitched battle the superior organisation and discipline of the Romans was decisive. Boudica and her rebellion were defeated and many of the Britons, including Boudica, were killed. Today, in many works of art and literature, Boudica is celebrated and immortalised as a brave warrior and freedom fighter. However, it should be remembered that she was also responsible for the deaths of thousands of innocent people and led her own people into bloody and disastrous conflict.

Changes

The village has a new name, a foreign name. Roads are dusty in the summer and muddy in the winter, just like before. You humans have a thing for names.

Something did change, though. The soldiers, brusque and conceited, with their red cloaks and vulgar jokes. They never left. They built their base near the ford, so that now they check everything and everyone that is carried along with the current. Whenever they need something, they take as much as they please, indifferent to the laws of men and gods. Whenever I have the chance, I drown a couple of them in the river.

Grata, Cocca's daughter, is six now. She is slender like a reed and very shy. She has a foreign name, too. Her father, Faustinus, is not from the village. He's a merchant, born far away, beyond the ocean. He has chosen her name, meaning 'welcome', to celebrate her coming into this world.

When she was two, Grata got terribly sick. Faustinus went out in a hurry, with a little bag of coins. A man came back with him, a military surgeon. He was tall and long-limbed, with a hooked nose and shiny, little eyes. He said there was nothing he could do. He said she was too weak, that she probably wouldn't make it through the night. He took the money and left.

Cocca then ran here and promised to kill two lambs for me. I would have saved her child for a bowl of milk. I visited Grata in her feverish dreams that night and told her to come back. At dawn, the fever was gone. In the crisp air of the morning, Faustinus himself sacrificed the beasts and poured their blood into the water, together with something else. A dark, purple liquor, strong like fire. Its rough taste made me strangely jolly and lightheaded for a while. I liked it very much.

This morning, Cocca is killing a goose. She is holding the plumed body firmly with her left arm and an axe in her right hand. The long neck of the goose lies on a stump. Grata caresses its head, whispering. When Cocca strikes, Grata looks away. She collects some of the blood for me. I accept it gratefully, by the white hands of this child I've saved.

Becoming Roman?

The concept of Romanisation underpinned studies of the Roman empire during the late 19th and 20th centuries. Archaeologists therefore focused largely on those aspects of Roman rule which were viewed as bringing 'civilisation' to the 'grateful' inhabitants of Britain, such as towns, villas, art and the Latin language. This work tended to emphasise a progressive evolution of culture under Roman rule and focused on those aspects which most closely approximated a 'Roman' identity; for example, archaeologists looked for similarities between towns, villas and mosaics in Britain and those found elsewhere in the empire. Distinctive local developments were often overlooked or downplayed. Recent archaeological research is challenging this over-simplistic notion, revealing the hugely varied, or discrepant, responses to Roman rule, and considerable continuity with the Iron Age. Impressive 1st-century villas, such as Fishbourne in Sussex with its richly appointed reception rooms, were the exception rather than the norm, and many towns and rural settlements developed in a rather *ad hoc* way according to local circumstances. The villa at The Ditches in Gloucestershire appears to have been built in the third quarter of the 1st century inside an Iron Age enclosure which also contained a roundhouse (a native British building type). The villa may have been constructed by the descendants of those who had first occupied the enclosure. They may have expressed their political affiliations and membership of the new Roman provincial social order through a new way of living, while maintaining a link to the location which had been important for their pre-conquest identity.

In Leicestershire, Nottinghamshire and Northamptonshire archaeological work in the major river valleys suggests much continuity between the Iron Age and the Roman era. The areas which experienced the greatest degree of change were those closest to the newly constructed roads and emerging towns. Small enclosed settlements were a common feature of many of the region's later Iron Age and early Roman landscapes and represent a continuation of local traditions. However, the degree to which this tradition remained the dominant one in the early Roman period is still unclear. While Roman shrines and other religious sites in the region are often found on, or very near to, Iron Age precursors, many Roman era settlements and farms appear to have been relocated from Iron Age sites. Some new settlements were established in the 1st and 2nd centuries AD as rural settlement was reorganised. Between the 2nd and 4th centuries this process saw the gradual rise of larger rural settlements, villas and 'village' like centres, as some of the smaller farms were abandoned in some, but not all, areas.

Roads connected Leicester with the wider Roman world. The Fosse Way, a major route across Britain from Lincoln (*Lindum*) to Exeter (*Isca Dumnoniorum*) crossed the River Soar at Leicester. From the south-east, the *Via Devana* connected Leicester with important Roman settlements in eastern Britain including Godmanchester (*Durovigutum*) and Colchester, while to the south-

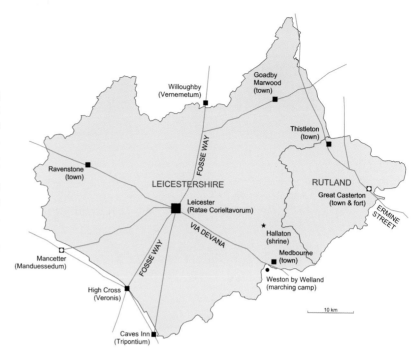

Above: Roman Leicestershire and Rutland, showing the main roads and settlements. Credit: ULAS

west other roads joined Watling Street, the major north-west to south-east route from Wroxeter (*Viriconium*) to St Albans, London and the ports at Dover (*Dubris*), Richborough (*Rutupiae*) and Reculver (*Regulbium*). Many of these roads exist and are used today: the Fosse Way is the A46, Watling Street the A5, and the *Via Devana* the Gartree Road. Small towns were established at Caves Inn (*Tripontium*), High Cross (*Veronis*) and Mancetter (*Manduessedum*) on Watling Street—all mentioned in the *Antonine Itinerary*—as well as at Medbourne on the *Via Devana* and elsewhere.

With the incorporation of the land of the *Corieltavi* into the new Roman province, significant reorganisation of the political landscape must have occurred in the late 1st century. A legionary fortress and later a *colonia* (a community of Roman citizens, largely retired soldiers) were imposed on Lincoln. By the end of the century, Leicester, as an already well-established and important late pre-Roman Iron Age settlement, was chosen as the new *civitas* capital of the entire territory. A *civitas* capital functioned as an economic and administrative centre for the collection of taxes and was governed by a council composed of members of the local elite. While the choice of Lincoln as a military base may have been strategic, the choice of Leicester as the regional capital may reflect how different groups of the *Corieltavi* reacted to the invasion. It is tempting to suggest that Roman objects found at Hallaton were gifts to a leader from the Leicester area who facilitated the Roman invasion.

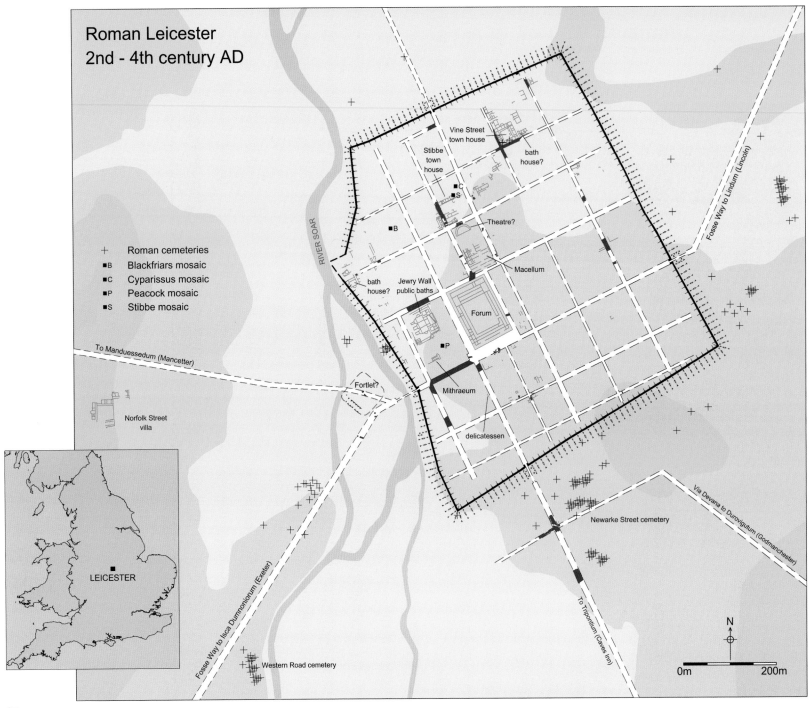

Roman Leicester
2nd - 4th century AD

Vine Street town house

Stibbe town house

bath house?

C
S

Theatre?

B

RIVER SOAR

Macellum

+ Roman cemeteries
■B Blackfriars mosaic
■C Cyparissus mosaic
■P Peacock mosaic
■S Stibbe mosaic

bath house?

Jewry Wall public baths

Forum

P

To Manduessedum (Mancetter)

Fortlet?

Mithraeum

delicatessen

Norfolk Street villa

Fosse Way to Lindum (Lincoln)

Via Devana to Durovigutum (Godmanchester)

Newarke Street cemetery

LEICESTER

Fosse Way to Isca Dumnoniorum (Exeter)

To Tripontium (Caves Inn)

Western Road cemetery

N

0m   200m

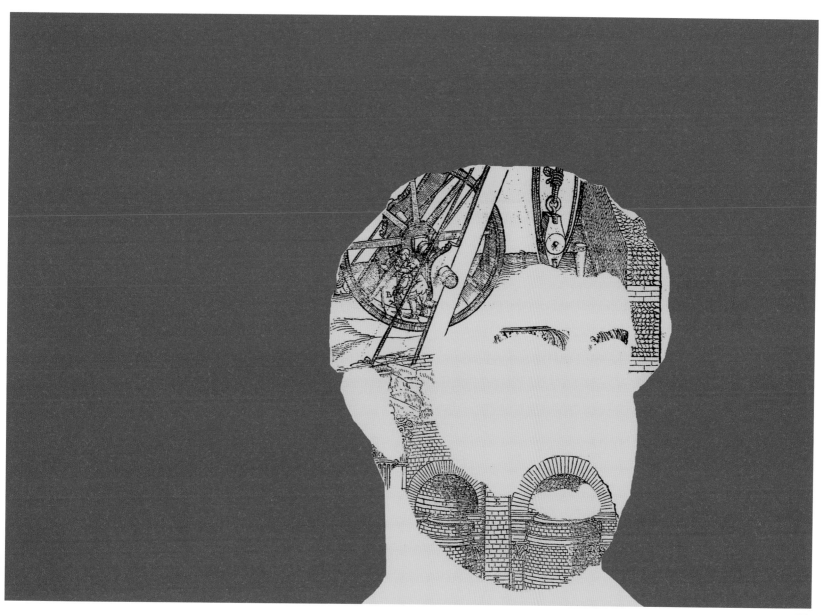

The City

Grata pours a cup of wine into the water. Her hands are spotted and creased now, they shake softly. Her eyes are milky and clouded like a winter sky. Yet, she smiles. She knows I'm smiling too.

She lived a long life. She was born in a tiny village and she is now breathing the foul air of a busy town, a suffocating blend of smoke, rubbish, and the waste of men and beasts. Before slipping into darkness, her eyes saw many things. They saw the construction of gravel roads, of grand buildings of bricks and stone, of temples and fountains. They saw the man who paid for many of them.

It was a chilly evening. A thick, stubborn rain pattered heavily on the parade helmets of the soldiers. The convoy was late. A clamouring crowd was gathered near the ford, at the two sides of a wide passageway rimmed with shields and spears. Finally, a rider appeared in the distance, escorted by a handful of guards in heavy, hooded capes. Several strides behind them, the road was thick with a multitude of men, carts, and horses covered in mud. When the rider got close enough, he raised his arm and the soldiers roared.

He was a sturdy man, with wavy hair and a short, well-trimmed beard. His tanned complexion had turned greyish in the cold wind of the north. He looked tired and worn, and yet a spark of determination was flashing in his dark eyes. The uproar of the soldiers rose. They were chanting his name, 'princeps princeps princeps'. Just like me, he had many names. Imperator Caesar Traianus Hadrianus Augustus. Someone could think he was a god too.

He remained here for only a few days, enough to inspect the foundations of the new town hall, to visit the richest men in town, and sacrifice to his gods. The day before leaving, he gave a long public speech. His gestures were measured and firm, his voice surprisingly piercing. He talked about the prosperity of the empire, about the long wall he was planning to build in the north, to protect us all from the barbarians.

Grata cannot remember his words. Her memories are fading away like shadows in a summer day. She cannot remember the names of her grandchildren either, but her ears are full of their bright laughter. She bends towards me, smiling. She says: 'I'm ready'. I gently grab her arms and take her with me into the dark water.

Roman cities

Urban centres were amongst the most important features of the Empire: they were focal points for administration and government in regions far from Rome. They were centres of commerce, and the buildings and monuments represented the physical embodiment of Roman ideals, values and ways of life.

Uncovering and interpreting the archaeological remains of urban centres is challenging due to the size of towns and cities and the variable nature of preservation and survival. Different Roman towns have been preserved under different conditions, and it can be hard to make comparisons. Two of the best known and most intensely studied towns are Pompeii and Herculaneum, which were preserved by the eruption of Mount Vesuvius in AD 79; they have therefore suffered relatively little disturbance in comparison to other towns. More commonly, towns were slowly rebuilt or abandoned with regular demolition of buildings, meaning that our understanding of their development is patchy. Many towns and cities have been continuously inhabited since Roman times, which means that archaeological remains are deeply buried. Rome itself is the best example of this, but it is also the case for many towns and cities in Britain, such as London and Leicester, where the Roman remains usually only come to light during construction work.

Rural life was celebrated by the elite because it represented traditional Roman ideals of self-sufficiency. The poet Juvenal (*Satires* 3), writing in the late 1st and early 2nd centuries AD, complained vociferously about the hazards and expense of city life, not least the imminent danger of death from criminal gangs or falling tiles. In contrast, Pliny the Younger (*Letters* 2, 17) praised the attractions of his country house at *Laurentum*, with its 'profound peace and seclusion', its 'well-stocked kitchen garden' and spectacular views of the sea. However, it was the city which was the hub of cultivated social and political life, and it was important for elites to live within easy travelling distance of an urban centre, where they often held political office and conducted business.

The Roman city was the centre of administration and local government, allowing the Roman state to assert its authority in distant regions. It was important to create a system that could represent central government and Roman political ideals in the provinces, in a period when long-distance communication was often slow and challenging. Each city was therefore administered along Roman lines, with members of the local elite elected to positions of authority on the local council (*ordo*, composed of *decuriones*). Certain facilities, such as the forum, with its council building (*curia*), *basilica* and other administrative offices, were required for this system to function efficiently and these were amongst the first elements to be established in any Roman town. While these distinctive and monumental elements could be found across the empire, from Palmyra to Leicester, there was nevertheless great diversity in the ways in which urban centres developed, and in the ways that both local and Roman identities were expressed through public architecture and art.

Above: Palmyra, situated in the Syrian desert, north-east of Damascus, was one of the most important cultural centres of the ancient world. The art and architecture of the city are a monumental amalgam of Graeco-Roman techniques and styles with local traditions and Persian influences. Credit: Simon James, University of Leicester

Roman Leicester (Ratae Corieltavorum)

Above: the Roman forum and basilica as they may have looked from the south-west during the early 3rd century AD. Credit: Mike Codd / Leicester City Council

Above: the central panel of the 2nd-century Peacock mosaic pavement discovered in 1898 on St Nicholas Street, now part of St Nicholas Circle. Credit: ULAS

By the early 2nd century AD the Iron Age and early Roman settlement Leicester had been reorganised and a new rectangular street grid, with drain ditches and cambered gravel roads, was laid out. This probably coinci with the settlement's appointment as the *civitas* capital of the Corie (*Ratae Corieltavorum*). From this time new and increasingly sophistica buildings begin to line the streets, and from the middle of the 2nd cen major programmes of public and private building were undertaken in town. Public buildings included the forum and *basilica*, the Jewry V public baths, and at least one temple identified as a *mithraeum* (dedicate the Persian god Mithras). Private buildings included a variety of dome commercial and industrial premises. Construction was not restricted to town, however, and large suburbs grew up, whilst substantial villas were b in the surrounding countryside.

The forum was a large open square with colonnades containing shops three sides and a large aisled building known as the *basilica* on the fourth. *basilica* housed offices and served as the town's administrative and judi centre. Today, what remains of the forum lies buried beneath Jubilee Squ Building the forum would have been a major undertaking, comparabl constructing a medieval cathedral or a modern skyscraper; it would h taken years to complete. When finished sometime in the middle of 2nd century AD, it would have measured some 132 by 91 m—larger t many football pitches. Small-scale excavations in the 1960s and '70s reve evidence for what the building looked like. Many of the rooms had cla concrete floors, giving the impression of a very functional building. L some rooms were redecorated with mosaic pavements and painted or mar veneered walls, and it is possible that traders were responsible for maintai and decorating their own shops. Some timber partitions were found wl may have been used as counters; other shops had small hearths which r have been for cooking food, providing warmth or serving industrial purp such as metalworking.

The area surrounding the forum contained a variety of public and pri buildings. To the west was the public bathhouse and Mithraeum, whilst to north commercial activity and entertainment had expanded out of the fo in the early 3rd century into a *macellum* or market-hall and a theatre. created a new retail quarter much like the Highcross shopping centre to Smaller commercial and domestic properties also surrounded the forum. the south, rows of timber and stone shops lined the street. To the east, fur substantial stone buildings were uncovered beneath the BBC building o Nicholas Place, whilst to the west was a substantial mid-2nd-century house (now beneath St Nicholas Circle) containing the Peacock pavem one of the finest mosaic floors discovered in Roman Britain.

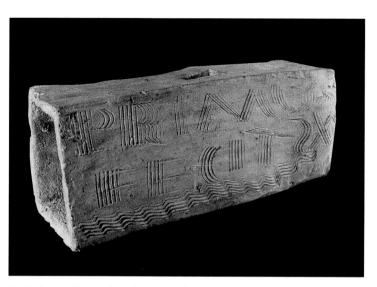

Above: Evidence for public entertainment in Leicester includes a sherd of pottery with the inscription VERECUNDA LUDIA LUCIUS GLADIATOR, *'Verecunda the actress' (or female gladiator) 'and Lucius the gladiator'. The hole suggests it may have been worn as a love token. Credit: ULAS*

Left: Primus, a tilemaker, wrote PRIMUS FECIT X, *'Primus made ten' (tiles), on this box flue before it was fired. Credit: ULAS*

In the late 2nd or early 3rd century, the town gained defences. At first these were simple ditches and earth ramparts with timber palisades, but a substantial stone wall was added to the front of the rampart in the late 3rd century. A section of the defences has been examined on Sanvey Gate, where two substantial ditches were found in front of a 3 m wide wall and interval tower. The wall may have been about 4 m high: as much a symbol of civic pride as a discouragement to would-be invaders.

By the late 3rd century, commerce was thriving and the town had established trade links across Britain and western Europe. New shops, workshops and houses were still being built in the 4th century. Despite this, the evidence suggests that large areas inside the town remained undeveloped. These open spaces probably served as storage yards, market spaces and kitchen gardens.

Right: Roman Leicester from the north-east, as it may have looked in the late 3rd century. Credit: Mike Codd / ULAS

Everyday life in Roman Leicester

Food remains show that people in *Ratae* enjoyed a varied diet. Barley and spelt wheat (used to make bread and porridge, and to thicken stews) were grown locally, along with peas, beans, leaf beets, apples, plums and cherries. Wild foods were also harvested, including hazelnuts, sloes, blackberries, elder and sorrel. People could season dishes with wild mint, coriander, opium poppy and mustard, whilst the wealthy could afford imported foods such as lentils and dried fruits. Meat mostly came from domesticated cattle, sheep, goat, pig and fowl, but wild deer, hare, geese and duck were also hunted. The fish that was consumed comprised mainly eels and herrings, although oysters too were a common food and were probably transported from the Essex coast. Finds of shell indicate that eggs were eaten, but other foods which must have been consumed, such as honey, milk and cheese, have left no trace. Some food was imported in large quantities: Olive oil, wine and fish sauce were transported across the empire in large storage vessels called *amphorae*.

Excavation of part of a Roman building near St Nicholas Circle has identified it as a 'delicatessen' selling both local foodstuffs, including smoked meats, and exotic imports such as figs, grapes and olives. Broken pottery found in a refuse pit behind the shops was unusual because it was mostly *amphorae*, bowls, jars and flagons but included no drinking vessels, plates or mixing dishes. This suggests food was not being consumed on the premises, like a tavern, but was being stored and displayed for sale.

The people of Leicester used pottery made all over the Roman empire. Pottery in Leicester came from Cambridgeshire, Warwickshire and Dorset, as well as from Spain, France, Germany, Italy and North Africa. Evidence for manufacturing in the town includes pottery, bone, iron, bronze, lead, glass and horn work; and evidence for a smithy and bone pin workshops was found at Vine Street (today beneath the John Lewis car park).

People also owned a wealth of personal items, which included jewellery, mirrors and tweezers, as well as everyday household items such as knives, spoons and *styli* for writing. Some of these were imported, but most were locally produced. Recreational items included musical instruments, bone dice and numerous gaming counters. Most of these were found by archaeologists because they were dropped and lost, or broken and thrown away. They show that the people of Leicester were as diverse and multicultural in their tastes as the city's inhabitants are today.

Above: Fresh meat and vegetables on sale in a Roman shop like the one found in Leicester. Credit: Mike Codd / Leicester City Council

Below: Some of the hundreds of personal items lost or thrown away by people in Roman Leicester. Found during the 2017 excavation of the former Stibbe factory site between Great Central Street and Highcross Street. Credit: ULAS

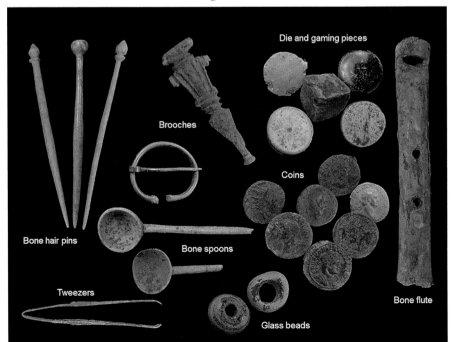

Hot water

The building is vast, with dense coils of steam rising from its bulky body of stone and bricks. The clamour inside is such that I can hear it from the river. I've been wondering for a while what was so special about this place. I came to see if there is any truth to what you mortals say: 'we have subdued fire and water to our will'.

I walk into a large hall, full of columns, marbles, statues. Naked people, too: soaking, swimming, chatting, drinking. And masseurs, ball-players, dancers, sellers, thieves. The entire city in one building. The more I proceed, the more the air gets heavy and thick with odours. Odours of bodies, cheap food, perfumed oils, and exotic unguents, all blending into the sweet stench of stagnant water. And the noise: a thunder of splashes, cries, calls, and gurgles, filling every room and ear. Yet there is more to it. Far from the madding crowd and the din of the main hall, a couple bathe together in the same pool and an old man indulges in puerile games, protected by the warm, spiced shadows.

I probe the water gushing from the mouth of a silver fish. It's hot like blood. I can feel the heat rising under my feet. I get into the last room, so steaming that the walls are covered in moisture. I plunge into the pool. Water embraces me like she has never done before, her dear touch turned suddenly unfamiliar. Fire has changed her, transfiguring her weightlessness into a heavy, suggestive substance.

And here, overwhelmed by hot vapours, I finally see why your princeps with many names has put so much money into this place. On the opening day, only a few of you knew what to do with it, and now you can't live without it. No one bathes in the river anymore, that's for the sick and the savage. I guess the war is really over now.

Taking the plunge

According to a 1st-century AD funerary inscription from Rome, baths are among the pleasures that *vitam faciunt*, 'make life worth living'. This brief text, together with many other epigraphic and literary sources from all over the Roman world, demonstrate the genuine appreciation of baths and bathing shared by people from diverse cultural and social backgrounds.

Bathing took place in many forms and settings, and bath buildings varied greatly in size and decoration. While even small villages had simple facilities, important cities of the Empire took pride in showcasing large and sumptuous bath complexes. The emperors were keen to associate their name with new, magnificent baths (also known as *thermae*), and the monumental remains of many of them can still be seen in Rome.

Most baths had at least three rooms: the cold room (*frigidarium*), the warm room (*tepidarium*), and the hot room (*calidarium*). In larger facilities, bathers could enjoy also a cold pool (*piscina*) and a hot, dry-steam sweat room (*laconicum*), similar to a modern sauna.

In Roman Britain, baths started to be built at military sites and rural villa sites soon after the conquest. By the middle of the 2nd century AD, most of towns were equipped with public baths. Customers did not use these buildings just to get clean; they went there to meet friends, chat and relax, exercise and conduct business. Ancient sources tell us that food was often sold near and inside baths and professional masseurs and beauticians treated their clients there. In this regard, they would now be considered similar to community centres, combining all the facilities provided by gyms, spas, libraries, shopping centres and restaurants.

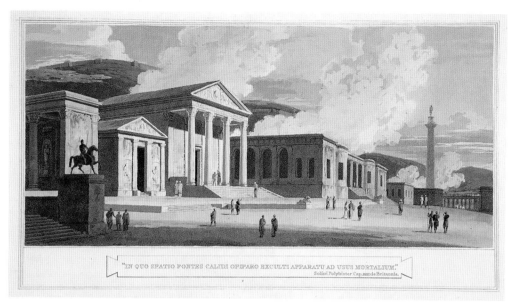

"IN QUO SPATIO FONTES CALIDI OPIPARO EXCULTI APPARATU AD USUS MORTALIUM."
Solini Polyhister Cap. xxii de Britannia.

Top right: Reconstruction of the temple at Bath. Samuel Lysons, Reliquiae Britannico-Romanae (1813), I, ii, frontispiece. Photograph by Colin Brooks. Credit: Special Collections, University of Leicester

Right: The cold room of the Stabian Baths in Pompeii. Credit: Wellcome Collection

The Jewry Wall Roman baths

Today, the only visible reminder of Leicester's Roman past is the Jewry Wall. It is one of the most impressive pieces of standing Roman masonry in Britain. It was formerly one of the walls of a large *basilica* containing the *palaestra* or exercise hall (where men could meet, box, wrestle and play ball games), attached to the town's public baths complex, which was built in the mid-2nd century AD. The wall, which still stands 8 m high, is built of alternating bands of thin Roman bricks and coursed masonry—mostly locally sourced volcanic rock from the Charnwood hills, with some local slate and sandstone, and millstone grit from Derbyshire. Small 'putlog' holes in the wall mark the position of the wooden scaffolding used during construction, and large arched openings in the centre of the wall are thought to have been doorways between the *palaestra* on the eastern side of the complex (most of which now lies beneath the church of St Nicholas) and the rest of the bath complex.

The central focus of the baths was the *tepidarium*, the warm room heated from under the floor through a hypocaust, where bathers could assemble and relax before moving on to the hot or cold baths—the *calidarium* or the *frigidarium*. Bathers covered themselves with oils and used a tool called a *strigil* to scrape off the dirt and oil. The three hot rooms were maintained at a temperature of about 40 °C. They contained pools of hot water which made them very humid, much like a modern sauna. The final step was to plunge into a pool of cold water, to close the pores and refresh the body.

The Jewry Wall baths were not the only baths in Leicester. Recent work beside the river, about 150 m north-west of Jewry Wall, has uncovered a large early Roman stone building built in the early 2nd century: almost certainly another bath house, possibly a precursor to Jewry Wall. The very wealthy could afford to have private bath suites attached to their own homes. A large Roman villa at Norfolk Street, about 600 m west of Leicester, probably had its own bath block. Another small bath suite containing a hypocaust-heated room and plunge pool formed part of a building, perhaps a house or small bath house, next to the Vine Street courtyard house in the north-east quarter of the town. Here construction work was not completed because of ongoing structural problems with the building and the bath suite was never used.

Above: A cut-away impression of how the Jewry Wall baths may have looked during the late 2nd century AD. Credit: Mike Codd / Leicester City Council

Left: The Jewry Wall. Once part of a Roman public bath house, today one of the largest surviving fragments of a Roman building still standing in Britain. Credit: ULAS

The Banquet

I've been invited for dinner in the house of a rich man. I didn't ask for it. It was the curious consequence of a present I made to a fisherman who lives just outside town. The largest barbel I've ever seen, nearly an arm long. I gave it to him for his children, but he decided to sell it instead and got good money out of it. He sold it to the slaves of Marcus, a veteran who came back with a small fortune after many years of service beyond the ocean. When he saw the fish, he was so pleased that he promised me a place of honour at his table.

And here I am, lying down sideways on this uncomfortable couch, covered in soft fabric, with a cushion under my left elbow and Marcus' father-in-law at my right. The old man is merry and noisy and, like the other guests, he's wearing light, colourful clothing. At my left there is another old man, a magistrate of some sort, with a golden ring on the little finger of his left hand. He's fat and bold, with tufts of red hair just over the ears and large, greasy lips. On the couch at my right, Marcus, with his pale complexion and bleary eyes, and his wife, young and chatty, together with a grinning young man that nods at everything Marcus says. The other three guests on my left are equally colourless and fawning.

We start with eggs, oysters, and honeyed wine, then the main course arrives: my fish, greeted with shouts and silly jokes. I look at it, disconsolate. The cooks have managed to spoil it with elaborate sauces and too much pepper. Everyone else is applauding, ecstatically.

After the offerings to the gods of the house, the slaves serve a strong, spicy wine and the magistrate, named Aelius, starts to tell stories with a furry tongue. He says that our beloved lord Severus, may the gods protect him, is here on our fair island, fighting against the barbarians in the north. He says that he's sick, though, and that something ominous happened to him in Luguvalium, while he was arranging the supplies for a new expedition. He wanted to sacrifice two white oxen to Bellona before moving north, but a rustic priest brought to him two black beasts instead. The great man drew back, horrified, and ordered those jinxes to be immediately released. Aelius pauses, dramatically. 'This is not all!' His shrill voice scratches the silence. 'They told me that the two beasts followed our good lord up to the door of his residence, making their mortal sign irrevocable.'

The guests, pale and incredulous, look at me for a comforting word. I say nothing, but the wooden face of my simulacrum on the couch smiles, benevolent, and Marcus puts a garland of flowers over my head.

Houses in the Roman world

There are many surviving written texts in both Latin and Greek which describe the kinds of activities taking place in Roman houses. The three authors who provide the most information about the types of rooms and their names are Vitruvius, in his *De architectura* (*On Architecture*); Pliny the Younger, who describes his villa in *Laurentum*, in Italy, in a letter to his friend Gallus; and Varro, who describes the origins of the names used for rooms in Roman houses within his *De lingua Latina*, a study of the Latin language.

Vitruvius' work is concerned with the proportions of the ideal house, the nature of different rooms and their locations (he was an architect working in the Augustan era). For example, he discusses rooms called *triclinia*, which can also be called *exedrae* or *oeci*, the length of which should be twice the width. The layout of his ideal house was symmetrical; the entrance corridor (*fauces*), led into the courtyard (*atrium*) with a central pool (*impluvium*), and then to the office (*tablinum*), and beyond it the garden (*hortus*). Other reception rooms (*alae*) and bedrooms (*cubicula*) surrounded the *atrium*. The view from the street was very important, and the visual axis through the house was often emphasised by columns and sculptures. Some houses in Pompeii, such as the House of Menander, have benches to the sides of the *fauces* for those waiting to visit the owner (*paterfamilias*). Literary sources reveal that large houses were very important for social and political success.

The Latin terminology often provides information about the kinds of activities which were carried out in rooms; for example, the word *triclinium* suggests a room with three couches, which would have been used for dining. However, other terms, such as *cubiculum* or *oecus*, tell us very little about the function of these rooms. When Pompeii was first excavated in the 18th and 19th centuries, the excavators often applied Latin names to rooms and objects uncritically without any supporting evidence. The archaeological evidence was largely used to illustrate the ancient texts which formed the basis of a classical education in this period.

In recent years, archaeologists and ancient historians have examined both literary and archaeological evidence together to understand better the complex relationships that existed between architecture, decor and social life. For obvious reasons much of this work has focused on houses in Pompeii and Herculaneum. Research has revealed that Roman houses were designed to emphasise and reinforce distinctions of social rank. The social status of the owner was further emphasised by interior décor and architectural features, such as mosaics, wall paintings and sculptures.

Atrium houses were largely unknown outside Italy. In North Africa, for example, many houses are classed as 'peristyle' houses and have colonnaded courtyards and central spaces without a roof. The form of houses across the empire depended on many factors, including earlier building traditions, availability of materials, relevant expertise (for example, the availability of architects and builders), resources, climate and personal taste. Houses across the empire often exhibit a fascinating and diverse combination of 'Roman' and local traditions.

Above: The House of the Surgeon, Pompeii: the courtyard, with an artist sketching the ruins. Etching by F. Piranesi, 1804, after G. B. Piranesi (1720–78). Credit: Wellcome Collection

The houses from Pompeii give us a good idea of what life was like in a medium-sized town in Italy before AD 79. However, because most of the evidence dates to the town's latest phases, and because Pompeii is very different to other sites in terms of its destruction, excavation and preservation, it is difficult to establish just how 'typical' these house are.

Living in Roman Leicester: the Vine Street courtyard house

One of the largest town houses found in Leicester, and the only house in the town where the complete floor plan is known, was the Vine Street courtyard house. Built in the early 3rd century, this spacious home measured 40 by 40 m, with four ranges of rooms linked by corridors surrounding a central courtyard. Of stone construction and roofed with diamond-shaped slates, it had at least 26 rooms, many of which were furnished with painted walls and concrete floors or mosaic pavements, whilst some rooms were heated under the floor through hypocausts.

The formal reception rooms faced the entrance and were surrounded by everyday living spaces and smaller, more utilitarian service rooms. In one corner of the building was a kitchen, and other rooms would have acted as dining rooms, sitting rooms, bedrooms and offices. The large courtyard could be viewed from all sides and contained an ornamental pool, and land behind the house may have been laid out as a garden.

The occupants were wealthy. Finds from late 3rd-century waste pits behind the house produced an extraordinary quantity of evidence for their lifestyle. In addition to staple foods such as wheat, their diet included a wide variety of local fruits, fish and meat. Game was served at table, and the occupants could afford imported fruits such as figs, sea fish and oysters. At one meal, a large freshwater fish known as a barbel, nearly half a metre in length, had been served.

Food and drink were stored and prepared in a wide range of bowls and jars including *amphorae* and *mortaria* (mixing bowls), before being served in fine-quality glass and pottery vessels and dishes. Many of the broken cooking pots still showed evidence of sooting on their exterior and limescale or other food remains on their interior. The occupants kept dogs, although whether they were pets or guard or hunting dogs is not known. They also owned a diverse array

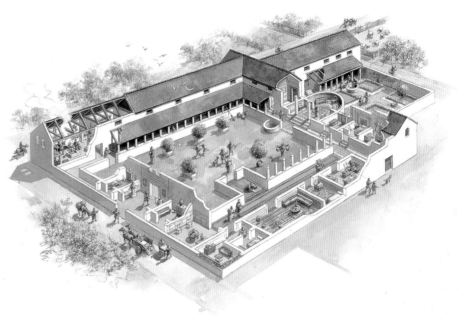

Above: A view inside the Vine Street courtyard house as it may have looked during the late 3rd century AD. Credit: Mike Codd / ULAS

of personal possessions, many dropped and lost, or broken and thrown away—jewellery including brooches, bracelets, hair-pins and finger-rings; toiletry items such as tweezers, nail cleaners and mirrors; as well as household equipment and recreational items, pins, needles, knives, spoons, spindle whorls, keys, gaming counters, figurines of household gods, ivory boxes and much more.

At one point, one of the owners may have been a high-ranking military officer who had moved or retired to Leicester, perhaps from another part of the empire. As well as the family, the household would have included servants and slaves, some of whom probably also came from outside of Britain.

The house was not a solitary building. It was situated in a thriving quarter and was surrounded by other homes, shops and workshops. In the 4th century a large warehouse was built behind the courtyard house, perhaps by the house owner to store their goods. Its construction broadly coincided with a fundamental change of activity in the area, with occupation starting to shift away from solely residential to more commercially orientated pursuits, signifying increasing commercial prosperity in this part of the town in the late 3rd and early 4th centuries.

The curious event involving the emperor Septimius Severus (AD 145–211) and his attempt to sacrifice two oxen to Bellona, told by Aelius during the banquet, took place in the northern town of *Luguvalium* (modern Carlisle).

It is based on a passage from the *Historia Augusta*, a collection of biographies of the Roman emperors written by different authors, perhaps in the 4th century AD. The reliability of this text as a source has been questioned by historians. However, the curious details and superstitious flavour of this episode give us a rare glimpse of everyday life in a remote outpost of the Empire.

Art in the Roman world

During the 18th century many scholars believed that Greek art represented the peak of human artistic achievement; Greek artists were admired for their ability to reproduce natural forms, especially the human body. Only the highest quality Roman art was deemed worthy of serious study. The most aesthetically pleasing objects were believed to be those of the Republic or early Empire because they most closely approximated the Greek ideal. Since the 18th century people have visited art galleries and museums to admire the ancient art on display, often focusing on its beauty or aesthetic qualities. It is easy to forget that these objects were part of the landscape of towns, cities, sacred sites and houses. 'Art' in the Roman world was present in all aspects of daily life.

The study of Roman art today is perhaps better described as the investigation of Roman 'visual material culture'. Their form is the result of a complex range of factors, including an individual's taste, experiences and resources, and the availability of materials and skilled labour. The visual material culture of the Roman world also included images on a wide range of everyday objects, such as terracotta lamps, carved hairpins, ivory boxes, engraved gemstones and coins.

Images were an important medium for conveying political messages in the Roman world. The emperor Augustus sought to express an idealised image of himself as the ultimate ruler. He wanted to be seen as a superhuman being with the power to salvage the Roman world from the chaos of the late Republic and to create a new golden age of prosperity. Augustus propagated the image of the ideal Roman family, prominently displaying his closest relatives as exemplars of Roman virtue. This emphasis on family values is

Above: Images of women and children from the imperial family on the Ara Pacis (Altar of Peace) in Rome. Credit: Carl Vivian, University of Leicester

Below: Drawing of one of the Ghirza carvings, showing a local chieftain receiving gifts. Credit: David Mattingly

evident on the *Ara Pacis* (Altar of Peace) in Rome (above), commissioned by the Roman senate to honour Augustus' return to Rome from *Hispania* (Spain) and *Gallia* (France).

Images of the imperial family were erected in the public spaces of towns and cities across the Empire, in the forum and *basilica*, in shrines and temples, as well as theatres and other entertainment facilities. Imperial portraits provide evidence of the ways in which images were used by provincial communities to express their Roman identity and links to the wider empire.

However, 'Roman' forms did not simply replace indigenous forms of representation. The situation was far more complex, with the interaction of cultures resulting in a diverse range of art which was shaped by individual choices and local circumstances (the Romans themselves adapted and incorporated forms from Greece and elsewhere). Archaeologists are exploring the ways in which these forms were shaped by local circumstances, and how they may have been displayed, viewed and interpreted.

The art found on the Roman-era tombs at the site of Ghirza in the Libyan pre-desert (approximately 250 km south-east of Tripoli) illustrates the complexity of provincial art. Many tombs include depictions of aspects of daily life which were believed to require the protection of ancestors. This reverence for the ancestors had a long history in the region, and continued throughout the Roman period, as evidenced by surviving tables and altars close to the tombs which were used in rituals to honour the dead. The art and architecture of the tombs is a fascinating fusion of Libyan, Punic (Carthaginian) and Roman forms; Carthage was an important ancient city located in what is now modern Tunisia. The art of Ghirza draws on Roman images of power but combines them with subjects, styles and ideas that were important locally.

Art in Roman Britain

The art of Roman Britain has often been viewed as second-rate. In the 19th century, the Trustees of the British Museum were primarily interested in Mediterranean classical antiquities as they worked to build a collection to rival those found in other European capitals. As a result, by 1850 all the antiquities of ancient Britain and Gaul could be collected in four cases in one room. As late as the 1870s, a 391-page guide, *A Handy-Book of the British Museum*, covered the Celtic, Roman and Saxon collections in just six pages. The remaining 385 pages were devoted to Assyrian, Egyptian and Classical antiquities. The most obviously 'Roman' art from Britain, such as mosaics and high-quality sculpture, attracted most attention.

Less spectacular examples of Romano-British art, including everyday objects which were often locally produced, received relatively little attention until the 1960s when an exhibition of the *Art of Roman Britain* was held in Goldsmiths' Hall in London in July 1961. This exhibition was important because it assembled a wide variety of Romano-British art for the first time. In the catalogue of the exhibition the eminent classical archaeologist Professor Jocelyn Toynbee enthuses about the overall impression created, which was 'that of an immensely rich intermingling in Britain of aesthetic tastes and standards, of patrons of very diverse types, and of subjects of widely differing kinds depicted in both native and imported works of art'. Since this period, archaeologists have increasingly focused on recording and explaining the disparate range of art in Britain, which often represents a complex and creative fusion of local and 'Roman' elements. A mixture of imported forms, as well as distinctive local traditions, is evident on everyday objects in Leicester, demonstrating a wealth of responses to Roman rule.

Above: Part of the 2nd-century Blackfriars mosaic. Discovered in 1832 at Jewry Wall Street, now beneath the former Leicester Great Central Railway station. Originally preserved in its original location, it was moved to Jewry Wall Museum in 1976. The magnificent mosaic was from a town house. It, the Peacock Pavement (page 34) and the Stibbe mosaic (page 12) were probably all made in the same Leicester workshop or mosaic school. Credit: © Leicester City Council

Far left: The bone handle for a folding knife. Found beneath the original Shires shopping centre in Leicester (today part of Highcross shopping centre). The upper part of the handle shows a small, grotesque figure, probably the Roman god Pan, holding a set of pan-pipes as if he is about to play. Credit: ULAS

Left: Bronze knife handle. Found at the Stibbe town house. This unique object is decorated with a bearded 'barbarian' figure, wearing trousers and belt, being attacked by a male lion. The barbarian stands on the heads of four naked male figures. It is thought to represent a rare damnatio ad bestias scene—condemned captives being killed by wild animals. Credit: ULAS

The Stolen Cloak

It's a small, light sheet of lead, with little letters scribbled all over it. A list of names. There is one of my names too, at the very front: 'daeo maglo', to the god Maglus. Servandus, Marcus' slave, gave it to me. It's hard to get the justice of men if you are a slave. So he seeks divine revenge, instead. My revenge.

He will be disappointed, though. I don't like him. He's proud and disdainful, even in his prayers. He's the personal slave of a rich man, lives in a fancy house and thinks of himself as someone of importance because he owns a slave himself. He beats the poor boy over the slightest thing, especially when he has been beaten by his master. He doesn't deserve my help.

Besides, I know very little about these people Servandus is accusing of having stolen his cloak. All slaves working in the same house, with their foreign gods they have carried along from far away. One of them, Senedo, has the same name as a boy I knew, a long time ago, but that's all he shares with him. When Felicianus arrived here, he made offers to the local deities, to be sure not to upset anybody. When the new moon comes, Cunovendus, sixteenth on the list, pours milk for the gods of the river, and I get to drink some of it too. None of them has ever talked to me, though.

Yet, there is someone I know. A little girl, Nigella. She was born in a land where the earth is dry and hot, beyond the ocean and the narrow sea. And yet, she has learnt of me. I wonder who told her about my place.

She comes at night sometimes, a shadow among the shadows. She has big black eyes and curly hair, her skin the colour of burnished iron. She talks to me in a foreign language, whispering like water. She tells me about the bright light of the south and the strange beasts that live in her motherland. Water-dragons and horses with long necks, birds that cannot fly and vast, large-eared creatures with a skin that is harder than stone. She tells me about the food, too. About the way her grandmother used to bake flat bread in shallow dishes early in the morning and the smell of bonfires and roasted meat in the mild summer evenings.

Once, Nigella told me about the night she was taken away. About the long journey packed in a cart with men and women and children, about the sweetish stench of the slave markets. About the man who bought her, the way he looked at her, like he was looking at a piece of carved wood. The words the slave trader said: 'She is warranted healthy and not liable to run away.'

Nigella is always cold here and she asks me to free the sun from the clouds, to make the rain stop. I tell her that I cannot, that I'm just a small god. Sun and rain do not listen to me. But a cloak, I say, that I can find for you.

Curse tablets

Throughout the Roman World, especially in Britain, writing a curse was a popular way of seeking divine punishment of a wrongdoer. The message was usually inscribed on a metal tablet which was then thrown into a sacred pool or hidden in a building. Many examples have been recovered from the sacred springs at Bath in Somerset and a Roman shrine at Uley in Gloucestershire. Today, such discoveries are hugely important because they reveal something of the voices of ordinary people which would otherwise be lost.

Two curse tablets have been found in Leicester, both at the site of the Vine Street courtyard house. At first glance the thin sheets of lead look unremarkable, but a closer look shows that both are inscribed with faint lines of Latin script. The script is one commonly used for everyday documents and letters and the style of the language suggests that they were written sometime between AD 150 and 250. They are the first written texts from Roman Leicester (apart from a few instances of graffiti).

One, known as the Servandus Tablet after the name of its writer, appeals to a Celtic god, Maglus, and lists the names of nineteen people suspected of a theft from a *paedogogium* (slave quarters). Translated, it reads:

> I give to the god Maglus him who did wrong from the slave quarters; I give him who did steal the cloak from the slave quarters; who stole the cloak of Servandus; Silvester, Rigomandus, Senilis, Venustinus, Vorvena, Calaminus, Felicianus, Rufaedo, Vendicina, Ingenuinus, Iuventius, Alocus, Cennosus, Germanus, Senedo, Cunovendus, Regalis, Nigella, Senicianus [*deleted*]. I give that the god Maglus before the ninth day take away him who stole the cloak of Servandus.

The tablet contains several significant pieces of information, including the first known reference to a god called Maglus, possibly a form of the Celtic *maglos*,

Above: Detail of the Servandus Tablet showing the neat Latin script inscribed on the soft lead. Credit: ULAS

meaning prince. The twenty people named on the tablet are the single largest group of people known to have lived in Roman Leicester. As the cloak was stolen from a slave quarters, the list is probably a unique roll-call of household slaves, probably from the courtyard house; mortar on the tablet suggests that it was originally placed in a wall. Amongst them are people with a mixture of Latin (e.g. Silvester), Greek (Alocus) and Celtic (Cunovendus) names, as well as seventeen men and three women (Vorvena, Vendicina and Nigella). The cloak itself was a *sagum*, a square cloak often worn by soldiers and their servants. Curiously, Servandus, or the scribe writing the curse on his behalf, crosses out the last name on the list, Senicianus. Had he established his innocence? Or was he guilty of the theft? We will never know.

The second tablet, the Sabinianus Tablet, refers to the theft of silver coins. It reads:

> Those who have stolen the silver coins of Sabinianus, that is Similis, Cupitus, Lochita, a god will strike down in this *septisonium*, and I will ask that they lose their life before seven days.

The *septisonium* mentioned here may be a monumental pillar or fountain depicting the seven gods after whom the Roman days of the week were named (the Sun and Moon, Mars, Mercury, Jupiter, Venus and Saturn). It is only one of a handful of known references to such a structure in the Roman Empire. Unfortunately, we do not know where it stood, although it was possibly close to the *macellum*, as a column with decoration typically associated with celestial deities was found there in the early 20th century.

The description of Nigella by the slave trader is taken from a tablet found in London in 1996: 'Vegetus, assistant slave of Montanus the slave of the August Emperor and sometime assistant slave of Secundus, has bought (…) the girl Fortunata, or by whatever name she is known, by nationality a Diablintian (…) for six hundred *denarii*. And that the girl in question is transferred in good health, that she is warranted not to be liable to wander or run away (…)' (translated by R. Tomlin). This legal document dates to about ad 80–120 and reveals the complexity of London's slave society at the time. Fortunata, who came from northern Gaul, was sold to Vegetus, himself a slave of Montanus, slave of the Emperor (either Domitian or Trajan). 600 *denarii* was a large sum, about two years' salary for a Roman soldier, and we might find it surprising that a slave had so much money at his disposal. However, Vegetus's privileges came probably from his role within the province's financial administration.

Religion in the Roman world

Roman religion was everywhere; it was diverse and coloured all aspects of daily life. Religious activities were performed in a range of different locations, and deities could be honoured in a variety of ways.

Among the many gods worshipped by Romans, three were of primary importance: Jupiter, Juno and Minerva, or the Capitoline triad (named after the Capitoline Hill in Rome where a temple to all three was situated). Jupiter was king of the gods, the god of law and social order and the patron deity of Rome; Juno was his sister and consort, goddess of marriage and birth and mother of several other deities. Minerva, a daughter of Jupiter, was goddess of arts, wisdom, warfare, medicine and commerce. The triad represented the aspirations of the Roman state, and temples built to the three deities (*capitolia*) in distant Roman provinces were a means by which a town or city could symbolise its allegiance to Rome. The Romans were not exclusive in their worship, however, and some of the deities encountered in conquered regions were brought into the Roman pantheon (collection of gods)—and even re-introduced back into conquered territories as Roman deities.

Central to religion in the ancient world was the need for direct communication between mortals and their gods. To keep in favour with the gods, mortals needed to demonstrate their respect by way of offerings that ranged from a small cake or some incense, to the construction of a statue or temple—or sacrifices, whether small (such as a bird) or large (for example, a bull). Rituals were usually performed on behalf of the population by elected priests, who were also responsible for maintaining shrines and temples and celebrating specific rites according to the public religious calendar. These officials were not, however, religious specialists; they were magistrates (civic officials) for whom a priesthood and its duties were among a range of other responsibilities. Religion was therefore closely linked to politics, status, wealth and power. Responsibility for the well-being and stability of a community, and of the Empire, was both a political and religious duty.

The performance of rituals was not, however, restricted to priests. Anyone could communicate with the gods through prayer or sacrifice to obtain

Below: The Pantheon (temple of all the gods) in Rome. Credit: Carl Vivian

divine favour. A curse tablet, such as the Servandus tablet in Leicester, was a form of prayer and request for divine favour to avenge wrongdoing. Many houses in Pompeii have a shrine to the family ancestors (*Lares*), which was a focus for family prayer and worship. Vesta (the goddess associated with cooking and the hearth), the *Penates* (spirits of the larder) and the guardian spirit (*Genius*) of the head, were also important household deities.

Religion was therefore bound up with the daily routines of individuals as well as the affairs of state. It was practised across a wide range of public and private spaces.

One of the most important aspects of religious change brought about by the contact between classical Roman religion and the cults and deities of conquered peoples was the reinterpretation of local gods. Often this process is described as syncretism, and in many cases appears to have involved pairing up local gods or goddesses with their Roman equivalent to create an acceptable new version of that deity. Deities who shared similar attributes were often associated with one another and came to be understood as a single entity. An example of syncretism is the goddess Sulis Minerva, worshipped at Bath (*Aquae Sulis*) in Somerset. Syncretism did not involve the creation of entirely new gods; instead, it was a process whereby localised forms of indigenous and Roman deities were produced in a manner that was recognisable and meaningful to all concerned.

In Leicester, there is evidence for the continued worship of local deities. The god Maglus (mentioned on the Servandus curse tablet) is not found anywhere else in the empire. There is also evidence of the adoption of Roman religious practices; a pit in the courtyard of the town house at Vine Street had deliberately placed deposits of red deer legs buried beneath a stone and tile pedestal, which was probably the base of a household shrine. Personal possessions from people in the town also show an array of non-British deities and religions from the eastern side of the Roman Empire: Mithraism and Christianity were well established.

Roman deities in Leicester

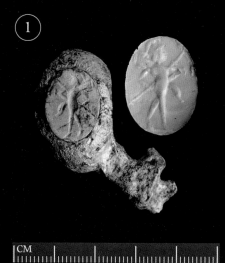

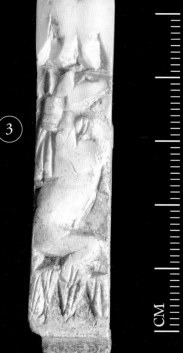

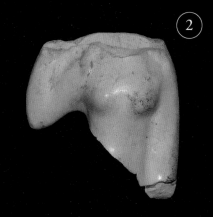

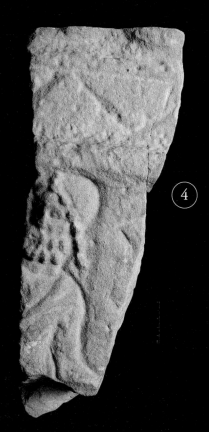

Monumental carvings and an array of personal possessions give a fascinating insight into the diverse pantheon of gods known about by inhabitants of the Roman town. This is demonstrated by the number of different deities found on objects during the excavations of the Vine Street courtyard house and the *macellum* site.

1. A once-splendid **silver intaglio ring** containing a semi-precious gemstone on which an image, or *intaglio*, had been carved depicts the Roman god Mars. At some point the ring was almost destroyed in an intense fire which has melted and distorted the silver, but the well-carved image survives. Mars appears naked apart from a helmet and cloak, and carrying a spear and trophy. He is in his persona *Mars Gravidus*, which the god was believed to adopt when guiding armies to victory. Rings like this were fashionable in the 1st and 2nd centuries, and the stone was probably red jasper.

2. The broken torso of a small **white-clay figurine** of the Roman goddess Venus. Cheap votive figurines like this were made in central Gaul and were frequently presented as offerings to the gods at temples and household shrines. Venus figurines were often associated with women during pregnancy and childbirth. When intact, it would have shown Venus holding a tress of hair in her right hand whilst her left hand clutched a cloth draped over or beside her leg.

3. A small **rectangular ivory panel** is an extremely rare object which depicts the Egyptian god Anubis squatting amongst lotus flowers and holding a lance. This panel was from a relief-carved ivory box, an exceedingly rare luxury item even in Egypt where it was made. It is remarkable that it made its way to Britain. Anubis was popular amongst Egyptian soldiers in the Roman army, and suggests that someone with a military connection may have been living in the house at Vine Street.

4. During the excavation of the *macellum* site (beneath the Travelodge on Highcross Street) part of a **stone altar** was found showing a bearded reclining figure wearing a robe and a distinctive fisherman's cap, possibly a water god like Oceanus.

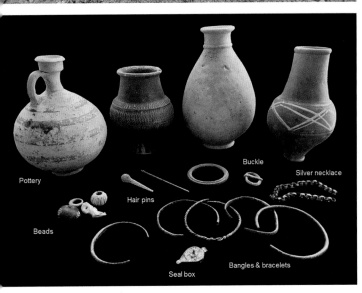

Above: Personal items buried with people in Leicester's western cemetery (today near Western Road). Burial rites in the cemetery suggest it was a 'pagan' cemetery. Credit: ULAS

Top: Archaeologists excavate skeletons in Leicester's southern Roman cemetery (today near Newarke Street). Burial rites in the cemetery appear to be mainly Christian. This might mean that Christians in the town were deliberately choosing not to be buried in the old 'pagan' cemetery across the river.
Credit: ULAS

Death and burial

The evidence available to archaeologists for burial in the Roman world is considerable. It reveals that burial practices varied over time and depended on the status and beliefs of the individual. Roman culture had emotionally conflicting attitudes towards the dead. On the one hand the corpse was regarded as polluting; on the other a major virtue in Roman culture was the veneration of ancestors. Burial was prohibited within the sacred boundary of the city (the *pomerium*)—although Cicero tells us that legally this was to stop funeral pyres causing house fires—so large cemeteries developed in the suburbs with elaborate grave markers and mausoleums lining the main approach roads. A Roman funeral typically had five parts: a public procession, often with professional mourners, actors and musicians (the more wealthy and famous the deceased was in life, the larger and flashier their funeral procession); the cremation or burial; a eulogy praising the deceased; a funeral feast; and annual commemoration by the family, often at set times of the year such as during the *Parentalia*, a nine-day festival honouring family ancestors.

The major change in burial practice over time was the gradual transition from cremation to inhumation from the end of the 1st century AD onwards. With the growing popularity of inhumation (the practice of burying the dead), burial pits became more varied. In some, tiles or stone slabs were used to roof the pit, in others, the body was covered by broken *amphorae* or bricks. Shrouds and wooden coffins were commonly used, whilst lead coffins and stone sarcophagi were used to a lesser extent, perhaps reflecting an individual's high status. With some burials, grave-goods (personal belongings and offerings for use in the afterlife) were carefully placed with the deceased.

Several large cemeteries have been excavated to the west, south and east of Leicester. The earliest was west of the city on the opposite side of the river. Burials stretched for at least 200 m along the line of the Fosse Way. A large number (83 skeletons dating from the late 1st to the late 4th century AD) were excavated between 2010 and 2015 at Western Road. Many were buried with grave-goods, or exhibited burial customs not seen elsewhere in the city—unusually, 12 were buried prone (face down) rather than supine (face up), whilst 'paired' graves suggest family plots. This has led archaeologists to suggest that the cemetery was used by the pagan residents of the town, who continued to use it, and their own burial customs, even after the Roman Empire had officially adopted Christianity in the early 4th century.

Tantalisingly, six people buried there may have had African ancestry, the first evidence ever found for Leicester's 'migrant' population. Two were born in Britain—one in the Leicester area and another in the Pennines area—whilst another, a child, almost certainly came from a sunnier, southerly climate such as around the Mediterranean. Archaeologists could determine this by studying their teeth to work out what type of water they drank in early life and where it originated from, a process called stable isotope analysis. Skeletons of African origin, dating from the same period, have been found at York and on Hadrian's Wall, but this is the first evidence in Leicester and shows that the Roman city may have been as diverse and multicultural as it is today. South and east of the city, Roman burials were very different in character. Roman suburban occupation of the 1st and 2nd centuries AD was superseded by cemeteries in the 3rd and 4th. Most of these graves were arranged in ordered rows, all on an east–west alignment. Few had grave-goods, and the burial rites more generally reflected Christian traditions.

A New God

Just outside the walls, not far from the river, there is a small cemetery. Only certain people are buried there, people that worship a new god. No food, wine, or musicians are allowed in there. Their ceremonies are simple and modest: men, women, even children are all buried in the same way, with their heads towards sunset, following the rules of their priests.

Their god came from the East not long ago, yet his followers are numerous here. No secret rites, no painful initiations are required and his community is open to all. Among them you'll find the rich and the poor, the magistrate and the slave. Quite an achievement, no doubt about it. Especially if it's true what they say, that this god died like a man. I thought gods could not die, only fade away gently, like mist in the sun. That's what will soon happen to me, I guess. I don't judge you for having forgotten me, though; your finite lives make you eager for hope and I've never had much of that coin.

On market days, the peasants, fishermen, and shepherds that come into town still honour me with wine and milk. They even teach my names to their children, but just a few of them dare talk to me. They are scared that I might drag them into the water and eat them. I don't know where these stories come from at all. Never had a taste for human meat, too lean and stiff.

Among the few children brave enough to talk to me, there is Map, the son of a farrier. He's direct and bold and tells me of how he once killed a rat with a single stone. He tells me of his sister too. She is crabby and a bully; she has stolen his clay whistle and broken it for fun. He wants me to eat her for dinner. I tell him I'll think about it.

Religions from the east

Mithraism

So far, only one definite Roman temple has been found in Leicester, probably a *Mithraeum*, a place where the Persian god Mithra or Mithras was worshipped. Within the Roman Empire, Mithraism was a popular mystery cult from the 1st to 4th centuries AD exclusively practised by men, and popular amongst soldiers and merchants. According to myth, Mithras created the world by sacrificing a bull. He was presented as a divine saviour who battled with the natural elements to bring order to the world and was closely connected with the order of the universe. His acts were depicted in the meeting place of initiates (a *mithraeum*) in the form of a relief sculpture, known as the Tauroctony. This scene showed Mithras wearing his distinctive Persian hat and cloak, and slaying the bull.

The temple in Leicester was found in 1969 to the south of the Jewry Wall Roman baths, during the construction of the Holiday Inn on St Nicholas Circle. The building was a small aisled hall, some 6 m wide and 15 m long, with apsidal (semi-circular) transepts and a possible 'sanctuary' at its eastern end, very similar to a church. The floor of the nave was sunken below that of the aisles and the walls were painted red. Niches built into the walls may have been for statues, and the layout of the building appears to have been designed for feasting and initiation, with worshippers gathering along reclining couches lining the walls. The temple was built in the early 2nd century AD, and coins found on its final floor suggest it remained in use into the late 4th century.

Top: The excavation of the Mithraeum in 1969, looking west down the nave with the raised aisle platforms to either side. Credits: ULAS

Bottom: A jet ring with a possible Christian iota–chi symbol, found in a Roman cemetery near Newarke Street

Christianity

The Roman Empire officially adopted Christianity as its dominant religion under the Emperor Constantine by the Edict of Milan in AD 313. Before this date Christian communities remained relatively small and disjointed, and were subject to periodic persecution, particularly during the 3rd century AD. Nevertheless, by the time of Constantine the church at Rome and its clergy were becoming increasingly wealthy urban landowners. Following the death of his father Constantius I, Constantine was proclaimed emperor of the western empire at York on 25 July 306. Marching on Rome in 312, he successfully defeated his rival, the emperor Maxentius, outside the city at the Battle of the Milvian Bridge, before entering the city in triumph. Christian sources later asserted that on the eve of the battle Constantine experienced a dream in which he was instructed to place the sign of God, the chi–rho (composed of the first two letters of ΧΡΙΣΤΟΣ, meaning 'Christ' in Greek), on the shields of his soldiers to ensure victory.

Evidence of Leicester's first Christians is elusive, but one clue may come from the burial of a woman in Leicester's southern cemetery (near Newarke Street). She was buried sometime between AD 355 and 420. There was evidence of a coffin in the grave and on her left hand she wore two rings, one made of iron and silver and one made of jet. The jet ring (left) had an enigmatic design on its bezel which resembles the Christian symbol iota–chi (IX), the Greek initials of 'Iesous Christos' (Jesus Christ). This interpretation must be treated with caution, however, as the additional cross-hatching in the opposing segments of the motif might instead argue for it simply being an attractive design.

Women and children

The family was at the heart of Roman life. However, Roman ideas of family were very different from those common in Britain today. Roman families were not simply defined in terms of blood ties (*cognati*), although the link between fathers and their children was important, especially in the spheres of inheritance and household religion. In a slave-owning society such as Rome, slaves were also an integral part of the household.

The most important social functions of citizen women, especially those of elite status, were perceived to be marriage and childbearing. There was no defined role for single young women in Roman society, so to remain unmarried was very unfortunate. Under Roman law women required the consent of their *paterfamilias* (head of family) to marry. Roman girls of privileged social status would often marry young, certainly before the age of 20, although the emperor Augustus established 12 as the minimum age for girls to marry. There was no legal requirement for a marriage ceremony, but celebrations usually included the procession of the bride through the streets followed by a banquet. Songs were sung and composed for the occasion. Some of these still survive, most famously the poet Catullus' hymn to Hymen Hymenaeus, the god of weddings.

The *domina* (wife of the *paterfamilias*) often played an important role in the management of the household, which in wealthy households included the supervision of domestic slaves and the control of household finances. For the wealthiest in society such duties could be extensive. It was not unusual for equestrians and senators to own numerous homes, estates and hundreds of slaves. In a letter to his aunt Calpurnia Hispulla, Pliny praises the domestic management skills of his wife, particularly the fact that her domestic spending habits were not too extravagant (*Letters* 4. 19. 1–2).

Women in Roman society were ideally meant to be socially subordinate. Throughout their lives women were at least notionally subject to a male authority; this could be their father, husband or *tutor* (male guardian). However, in the late Republic and early empire, the social position and freedoms open to Roman women increased, especially in respect to property. Women could own property in their own right; although legally binding contracts had to be backed by a male *tutor*. Female members of wealthy families could acquire vast personal fortunes through inheritance.

Above: Two votive statues of a Roman woman breastfeeding a child. They may have been intended to ensure a safe delivery during childbirth. Credit: Wellcome Collection

Procreation of the next generation of citizens was generally regarded as the aim of marriage. Childbirth was fraught with danger; most births would have taken place at home, and the mortality rate for infants and mothers was high. In Roman Leicester approximately 25% of the population died in childhood. The birth of a healthy child was a cause for celebration. The front door of the house was adorned with a laurel wreath, and special fires and altars were lit (Pliny the Elder *Natural History* 15. 127–138). If the infant survived long enough to be able to open its eyes and to focus, the ceremony of the *lustratio* was held. At this point the child received its *bulla*, a special pendant worn around the neck to ward off evil spirits. The infant was also formally granted a name for the first time (Suetonius *Life of Nero* 6).

Until recently, social histories have tended to focus on the main political events of Roman history, rather than on the impact these events had on ordinary people. It is also important to remember that sources describing the lives of women and children were written by and for elite males and often reflect ideals rather than social reality. Archaeological evidence, on the other hand, can provide important insights into the everyday lives of women and children. For example, excavations at Roman forts have shown that, while soldiers were not legally permitted to have wives while still on military service (until the 3rd century AD), women and children did live in and around military bases. These women were probably of different statuses, and may have included female slaves but also the wives and families of the soldiers, as well as women involved in commercial and industrial activities.

Other forms of tacit evidence, such as spinning and weaving tools, can show us the importance of female labour to the household economy. Funerary plaques and wall paintings show women working as shopkeepers, waitresses, hairdressers, jewellery makers etc. Outside the upper classes women probably had to earn a living or help towards the family economy, but their voices are seldom heard. Likewise, we know little of the experience of childhood, but the survival of toys demonstrate that some form of childhood play existed. The Romans mourned the deaths of their young children and recorded them with emotive language, such as *carissimus* (most cherished), and carefully recorded exact ages in years, months and days, suggesting they treasured every moment.

Twilight

Map is fifty-three now. He still comes to my place sometimes and tells me the stories he hears from the soldiers that visit his workshop. That's how I know about the usurpers and the rebels, about the raids on the coasts, about the turmoil on the Continent. About the young emperor and his valiant guardian, whom he killed out of jealousy. Map makes fun of him, says he cares more about his chickens than about his people, and laughs loudly with me.

Today, Map doesn't smile. 'The soldiers', he says, 'They don't pay me anymore'. His eyes restlessly scan the dark water, trying to read the expression on my face. He's upset, scared even. He doesn't know what this means. For him, for his children. I don't know either.

In the following months, some people leave. In small groups, a few at a time. Map has lost many of his clients. He's thinking of leaving too. He wants to get to the coast and buy a ride on a merchant ship, for him and his family. It's just a few hours' crossing and reasonably safe at this time of the year. He asks me if I want to go with them.

For a moment, I waver. I look at the river, at the familiar shape of the trees. At the town I have got so used to, with its tall walls and dusty streets. Then I think about the children that will not have a chance to go anywhere; the children of the farmer, the fisherman, the slave. I know many of them are scared of me, but at least they remember me. I say nothing and Map understands. He pours some milk in the water, waves to me and leaves.

The sun is setting slowly, lighting the water with purple and gold. I breathe the sweet smell of milk, wondering if I'll ever get to taste it again.

Unrest in the West

In the late 4th century and the early years of the 5th, there was significant political upheaval within the Roman empire. By AD 410 the remaining troops and government officials had been withdrawn from Britain, and the province was left to defend itself from increasing numbers of raids by barbarian tribes. We can only guess what effect this had on life in Roman Britain. Although the inhabitants perhaps tried to carry on as normal, the monetary economy must have collapsed quite quickly as trade with the Roman Empire dramatically declined, and coin supplies from the Continent dried up. Without civic authority, public building and streets must have fallen into decay.

Traditionally, this period (roughly AD 400–700) has been viewed as a period of decline or even a 'dark age', when Roman towns either disappeared or degenerated to such an extent that the term 'town' hardly seems appropriate. More recently, however, archaeologists and historians have adopted a more positive perspective in which the period is seen as one of transformation and cultural change, culminating in the development of the urban centres of the Early Middle Ages and subsequently the emergence of modern Europe. There are, however, many limitations with the written and archaeological sources for this period. For example, there are virtually no surviving written sources for Britain and parts of northern Gaul. In other regions of Europe where we do have written sources, many of these provide little information about the appearance or nature of activity within towns, and instead are more concerned with bishops and saints and their churches. Whilst we know from various sources that the *civitates* survived across most of western Europe (with the notable exception of Britain), they tell us nothing about how people lived within them. We do know from the archaeological evidence that there was considerable regional variation, and that many towns in Britain, such as *Corinium* (modern Cirencester) were thriving into the late 4th century and possibly beyond.

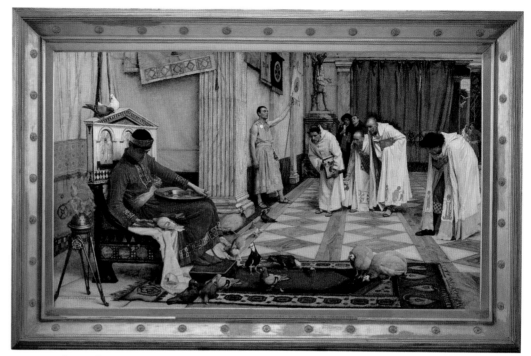

Above: The Favourites of the Emperor Honorius, *by John William Waterhouse (c.1883).*
Credit: Art Gallery of South Australia, Adelaide, with permission

Map is making fun of the emperor Honorius (AD 384–423). Honorius was only nine years old when he became emperor in 393, assisted by Stilicho, one of the last great generals of the western Roman Empire. Unfortunately, in 408, at the instigation of one of his ministers, Honorius ordered the execution of Stilicho. Two years later, in 410, Rome was sacked by Alaric, the King of the Visigoths. Rome was no longer the capital of the Empire at this time, which had moved to Ravenna in 402; nevertheless, it was still the premier city and spiritual centre of the empire. The sack, the first time in almost 800 years that Rome had fallen to a foreign enemy, was a massive shock to contemporaries, highlighting the increasing vulnerability and military weakness of the Western Empire.

The historian Procopius of Caesarea (c. AD 500–54) considered Honorius a terrible ruler and reports a piece of 'fake news' about him: 'At that time they say that the Emperor Honorius in Ravenna received the message from one of the eunuchs, evidently a keeper of the poultry, that Rome had perished. And he cried out and said, "And yet it has just eaten from my hands!". For he had a very large rooster, Rome by name; and the eunuch understanding his words said that it was the city of Rome which had perished at the hands of Alaric, and the emperor with a sigh of relief answered quickly: "But I, my good fellow, thought that my fowl Rome had perished." So great, they say, was the folly with which this emperor was possessed' (translated by H. B. Dewing).

Rome was sacked by Germanic tribes again in 455 and finally, with the overthrow of the last Roman Emperor, Romulus Augustulus in 476, the Western Roman Empire collapsed.

Leicester in the 4th and 5th centuries

What happened in Leicester in the 4th and 5th centuries is unclear. This is largely because medieval cultivation and quarrying of Roman remains for building material has destroyed much of the evidence. It used to be thought that Leicester entered a prolonged period of decline from the mid-4th century onwards. This was typified by the deterioration of public buildings like the forum and the *macellum*, which were becoming increasingly derelict with plaster falling from the walls, soil accumulation inside and some rooms suffering serious fires. Changes in the prosperous courtyard house on Vine Street saw the deliberate demolition of its main reception rooms and the conversion of the remaining building into a row of workshops, including a smithy. The discovery of hidden valuables carefully concealed in the ruins of the house, including a very large ingot of recycled lead and a hoard of coins dated to between AD 320 and 335, suggests that people were afraid of social unrest.

However, although the demise of the courtyard house gives the impression that there were fewer inhabitants in this part of town than hitherto, this is far from the case. The area was not abandoned, but rather it was rapidly redeveloped into a busy industrial quarter housing a wide range of craft activities. Next to the house, the large building, possibly a warehouse, appears to have prospered in this period, with new rooms and a walled yard added in the second half of the 4th century. Numerous late 4th-century coins were recovered, suggesting that the building was in use towards the end of, and possibly after, the official Roman government of Britain ended in AD 410.

Evidence from recent excavations in Leicester shows that the Roman city still had a functioning economy at the end of the Roman period. What was previously viewed as evidence of decline is anything but that. Instead, the conversion of high-status domestic occupation into manufacturing sites, and the evidently contemporary neglect of public buildings, probably suggest that it was the wealthy, urban-dwelling aristocracy who were abandoning town life. This may have resulted in the downgrading of public and monumental architecture, rather than a broader and terminal decline of the settlement. A large population probably remained, with many urban functions remaining intact, and Leicester probably continued to act as a regional focus for administration, tax collection and trade, and as a military strongpoint, into the 5th century AD.

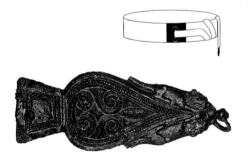

A late Roman military belt set from the Roman cemetery at Western Road, Leicester. Credit: ULAS

A Late Roman soldier in Leicester

Leicester's importance in the late Roman period is perhaps demonstrated by the presence of a high-ranking late Roman soldier or civil servant buried in its western cemetery (at Western Road).

The grave in question contained the remains of a middle-aged man wearing an elaborately decorated waist belt (*cingulum militare*) of late 4th- or early 5th-century style.

Although the leather had long since rotted away, the components themselves—a buckle, a belt plate and a strap end—are stunningly well preserved. The bronze belt plate, cast in so-called 'chip-carved' style, is decorated with interlocking spirals, and would have been fixed to a wide leather belt using rivets. A thinner securing strap would have run through the buckle and ended in the strap end, on which a pair of crouching dogs can be seen.

It is a unique find in Leicester, with only a few parallels in Britain and northern Europe. Pictorial evidence from frescoes and carvings suggests that the free-hanging strap end and the front part of the belt were normally visible beneath the folded-back cloak and were used extensively for display. Military belts such as this became expressions of a soldier's individual taste, wealth and special social status, but also of his identity as a soldier: from the 3rd century, the *cingulum* became a marker of military service. These belts were also worn by members of the civilian elite, representing important symbols of authority among public officials.

Injuries to the man's left forearm and wrist, which were left weakened, and damage to the muscles in his right upper arm and shoulder, make it doubtful that he was still a soldier when he died. Instead, he had probably retired from the army before becoming a high-ranking local civil servant.

Ruins and memories

So little remains of these great halls. Wind and rain have scratched away the bright colours that once covered their mighty walls. Hollow sockets full of rubbish have replaced the marble pools, once full of hot, foreign water. Around me, piles of bricks and plaster, soaked and stained with red. Under my feet, fragments of chipped roofs, torn, fallen. The work of men is decaying, defeated by time and its incessant bustle.

Yet, there is life among these ruins. Under the cracked ceiling of a vault, a wren has made its nest. Tender shoots of beech grow in the interstices of the mosaic floors. Where the tall columns once stood, an old woman has made a shelter for herself and her pigs. She talks to them and brushes their bristly hair with a bone comb. She's never killed one. Once a day, a man comes to bring her some food and exchange a few words. He's tall and handsome, often with a bow over his shoulder and a green cap on his head. He speaks very little of her language but cares about her.

He's one of the newcomers from the east. They keep coming, in small groups of two or three families, with their horses and carts. They're good carpenters and build sturdy houses of wood. When their women come to the river to do the washing, they sing mild, monotonous tunes. They know I'm watching them and leave hazelnuts and bread for me on the shore.

When summer comes, their children bathe in the river, just like the children of those that were here before. I have a new name now, a name you'll soon forget once more.

The end of Roman Leicester and the arrival of the Anglo-Saxons

The early years of the 5th century AD saw considerable political unrest within the western Roman empire. By 410, the remaining Roman troops and government officials had withdrawn or been expelled from Britain and the Emperor Honorius had told the British to look to their own defence against increasing numbers of raids, particularly from the Angles, Saxons and Jutes from what is now northern Germany and Denmark.

At present, it is not possible to recognise and date any activity at all between 400 and 450 on archaeological sites in Leicester, but this is probably because the inhabitants of the city were still making and using the same pottery and other objects as they had before. It used to be thought that thick layers of dark soil found above the last Roman levels showed that the town was abandoned, but scientific analysis now suggests that this accumulated as a result of domestic occupation and the keeping of animals. Within the walls of Roman Leicester, the appearance of distinctive hand-made pottery and other finds, such as brooches and bone combs, would seem to indicate the arrival of Anglo-Saxon settlers in the later 5th and 6th centuries. Quite what effect this had on the pre-existing population is not entirely certain, but perhaps they gradually became integrated with the newcomers and began to adopt their objects and way of life.

A large area in the north-east quarter of the Roman town, beneath the Highcross shopping centre today, appears to have been a particular focus of

settlement in the early Anglo-Saxon period, perhaps because it was an area of open ground in the still-walled town which had not been fully developed. Timber buildings with floors suspended over large pits, probably used for storage or insulation, were constructed alongside larger timber halls. Whilst some of these 'sunken-featured buildings' may have been lived in, most would have been used as workshops, particularly for the manufacture of textiles. This is based on the discovery of objects associated with weaving, such as loom weights, spindle whorls and combs. One of these buildings, near Highcross Street, was constructed in the rubble of the east wall of the Roman *macellum* which had collapsed at some point in the 5th century (above).

Although it is unlikely that the first Anglo-Saxons to have lived in Leicester occupied anything like what we (or the Roman inhabitants) would have recognised as a town, the community must have flourished as Leicester has remained continuously occupied to the present day.

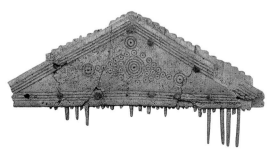

Above: An Anglo-Saxon building found near Highcross Street. It was built on fallen masonry next to the ruined Roman macellum in the 5th–6th centuries AD. Credit: Mike Codd / ULAS

Left: An Anglo-Saxon bone comb found in Leicester

References

Ainsworth, J., Savani, G., and Taylor, K. 2018. *Life in the Roman World: Ratae Corieltavorum*. Leicester Classics Hub: Resources for Teachers. http://hdl.handle.net/2381/42447

Allison, P. 2013. *People and Spaces in Roman Military Bases*. Cambridge: Cambridge University Press.

Allison, P. 2001. 'Using the material and written sources: turn of the millennium approaches to Roman domestic space', *American Journal of Archaeology*, 105 (2), 181–208. doi:10.2307/507270

Beard, M. 2015. *SPQR. A History of Ancient Rome*. London: Profile Books.

Brookman, H. 2016. 'Gurney, Anna (1795–1857)', *Oxford Dictionary of National Biography*. Oxford: Oxford University Press. https://doi.org/10.1093/ref:odnb/11759 (accessed 17 Feb. 2017).

Caygill, M. 1996. *The Story of the British Museum*. London: British Museum Press.

Christie, N. 2010. *The Fall of the Western Roman Empire. An Archaeological and Historical Perspective*. London: Bloomsbury Academic.

Fitzpatrick, A. 2018. 'Ebbsfleet, 54 BC: searching for the launch site of Caesar's British invasions', *Current Archaeology* 337, 26–32.

Haverfield, F. 1907. *The Romanization of Britain*. Oxford: Oxford University Press.

Henig, M. 1995. *The Art of Roman Britain*. London: Batsford.

James, S. 2011. *Rome and the Sword: How Warriors and Weapons Shaped Roman History*. London–New York: Thames & Hudson.

Mattingly, D. 1997. 'Introduction', in D. J. Mattingly (ed.), *Dialogues in Roman Imperialism: Power, Discourse, and Discrepant Experience in the Roman Empire*. Ann Arbor: Journal of Roman Archaeology.

Mattingly, D. 2003. 'Family values: art and power at Ghirza in the Libyan pre-desert', in S. Scott and J. Webster (eds), *Roman Imperialism and Provincial Art*. Cambridge: Cambridge University Press. Pp. 153–170.

Mattingly, D. 2004. 'Being Roman: expressing identity in a provincial setting', *Journal of Roman Archaeology* 17, 5–26.

Mattingly, D. 2007. *An Imperial Possession: Britain in the Roman Empire 54 BC–AD 409*. London: Penguin.

Mattingly, D. 2011. *Imperialism, Power and Identity: Experiencing the Roman Empire*. Princeton: Princeton University Press.

Morris, M., Buckley, R., and Codd, M. 2011. *Visions of Ancient Leicester*. Leicester: University of Leicester Archaeological Services.

Savani, G. 2017. 'Rural baths and bathing: socio-cultural interactions in the Romano-British countryside', unpublished PhD thesis, University of Leicester. http://hdl.handle.net/2381/39975

Score, V. 2013. *Hoards, Hounds and Helmets*. Leicester: University of Leicester Archaeological Services.

Scott, S. 2012. 'Fourth-century villas in the Coln valley, Gloucestershire: identifying patrons and viewers', in S. Birk and B. Poulsen (eds), *Patrons and Viewers in Late Antiquity*. Aarhus: Aarhus University Press. Pp.183–212.

Scott, S. 2013a. 'Pioneers, publishers and the dissemination of archaeological knowledge: a study of publishing in archaeology 1816–1851', *Internet Archaeology* 35. https://doi.org/10.11141/ia.35.1

Scott, S. 2013b. 'Samuel Lysons and his circle: Art, science and the remains of Roman Britain', *Bulletin of the History of Archaeology* 23 (2), 1–22. http://doi.org/10.5334/bha.2323

Scott, S. 2014. 'Britain in the classical world: Samuel Lysons and the art of Roman Britain 1780–1820', *Classical Receptions Journal*, 6 (2), 294–337. https://doi.org/10.1093/crj/clt030

Scott, S. 2017. ' "Gratefully dedicated to the subscribers": the archaeological publishing projects and achievements of Charles Roach Smith', *Internet Archaeology* 45. https://doi.org/10.11141/ia.45.6

Scott, S., and Webster, J. eds 2003. *Roman Imperialism and Provincial Art*. Cambridge: Cambridge University Press.

Taylor, J. 2007. *An Atlas of Roman Rural Settlement in England*. (CBA Research Reports, 151.) London: Council for British Archaeology.

Toynbee, J. 1962. *Art in Roman Britain*. London: Phaidon.

Trow, S., James, S. and Moore, T. 2009. *Becoming Roman, Being Gallic, Staying British*. Oxford: Oxford University Press.

Level 1 Distance Learning Module. *AH1551 Introduction to Roman History*. Written by R. Bennett, with A. Merrills and R. Young. School of Archaeology and Ancient History, University of Leicester, 2013.

Level 2 Distance Learning Module. *AR2556 Archaeology of the Roman World*. Written by E.-J. Graham. School of Archaeology & Ancient History, University of Leicester, 2012.